Lab Manual

AP* Experimental Chemistry

EIGHTH EDITION

Steven S. Zumdahl

University of Illinois at Urbana-Champaign

Susan A. Zumdahl

University of Illinois at Urbana-Champaign

Prepared by

John G. Little

St. Mary's High School, Stockton CA

James F. Hall

University of Massachusetts Lowell

*AP and Advanced Placement Program are registered trademarks of the College Entrance Examination Board, which was not involved in the production of and does not endorse this product.

BROOKS/COLE
CENGAGE Learning

Australia • Brazil • Japan • Korea • Mexico • Singapore • Spain • United Kingdom • United States

For product information and technology assistance, contact us at **Cengage Learning Customer & Sales Support, 1-800-354-9706**

For permission to use material from this text or product, submit all requests online at **www.cengage.com/permissions** Further permissions questions can be emailed to **permissionrequest@cengage.com**

ISBN-13: 978-0-547-16867-8
ISBN-10: 0-547-16867-5

Brooks/Cole
10 Davis Drive
Belmont, CA 94002-3098
USA

Cengage Learning is a leading provider of customized learning solutions with office locations around the globe, including Singapore, the United Kingdom, Australia, Mexico, Brazil, and Japan. Locate your local office at: **www.cengage.com/international**

Cengage Learning products are represented in Canada by Nelson Education, Ltd.

To learn more about Brooks/Cole, visit **www.cengage.com/brookscole**

Purchase any of our products at your local college store or at our preferred online store **www.ichapters.com**

Printed in the United States of America
2 3 4 5 6 7 8 9 10 15 14 13 12 11

AP* Experimental Chemistry
Table of Contents

AP* Experimental Chemistry

To The Student

You are about to embark on what may very well be the most challenging course that you will ever take in high school. If you have taken other AP courses, you know that the College Board, the governing body of the AP program, sets very precise guidelines for the material to be covered. In the case of AP Chemistry, these guidelines extend to the laboratory program. Don't look on these experiments, therefore, as just activities. Each one has specifically been chosen and designed to address topics, reaction types, and specific items of chemical knowledge that you will need to master as you prepare for the AP Chemistry Examination. That doesn't mean that you can't enjoy yourself, though. Lab is the fun part of chemistry, in which you actually get to do the reactions that your text describes, so approach each experiment with interest and curiosity.

The schedule will be tight. Depending on the schedule of your particular school, you will probably have tight time constraints for getting labs done. You can help yourself immensely by reading the entire experiment a day or so before you are to do it. Each experiment has two parts that are designed specifically to help you prepare: the Prelaboratory Assignment directs you to prepare data tables and such in your notebook, while the Prelaboratory Questions are designed to focus your attention on the main points discussed in the body of the experiment. Some of the experiments in this manual cannot be completed in a single laboratory session. A compound that you prepare may need to dry overnight before you proceed, or you may need to do one part of an experiment on the first day, then complete it the next. Your teacher will tell you when that occurs, but assume that if you aren't told in advance that a lab is to cover parts of more than one laboratory period, you should make certain that you work efficiently to complete your assignment in the allotted time.

The assumption is that you have already taken one course in high school chemistry, so you know what purpose most of the equipment serves and how things like the balances work. If such is not the case, be assured that your teacher will give you all of the information and instruction that you need to have a successful laboratory experience.

The next few sections of this Preface address specific topics concerning your laboratory work for the coming year. Each is brief and general, so it is up to you to be familiar with the specific rules and policies of your teacher and of your school.

The Laboratory Notebook

Increasingly, colleges and universities are requiring that students who have taken AP Chemistry and have passed the AP exam be able to show proof that they also had a full laboratory experience. For that reason, you will be required to keep a bound laboratory notebook. Most notebooks have carbonless duplicate pages, so that you can keep the original and turn the copy in to your teacher for grading. There are some general rules that apply to your notebook, whether or not it has duplicate pages.

All of your records go here. If you had report sheets that you filled in as you worked, then handed in as your write-up for labs in your first chemistry course, that will no longer be the case. All of your data and observations, as well as your answers to questions, go in the laboratory notebook.

---

*AP and Advanced Placement Program are registered trademarks of the College Board, which was not involved in the production of and does not endorse this product.

You are not to remove pages from your notebook. It is a "living record" of what you did, the observations you made, and the conclusions that you drew based on those observations. If you make a mistake, draw a single diagonal line through the part that is incorrect, then make the necessary corrections in the space that follows. This also means no white-out.

Safety

Chemistry is an experimental science. You cannot learn chemistry without getting your hands dirty; you already know that from your first chemistry course. It would be untruthful to say that there is no element of risk in a chemistry lab. *Chemicals can be dangerous.* The more you study chemistry, the larger the risk will become. However, if you approach your laboratory work calmly and studiously, you will minimize the risks.

Before the first laboratory meeting, you should refresh yourself on the safety lessons you learned before. If your AP Chem class uses the same lab room that you used in your first chemistry course, great! You know your way around. Close your eyes, and test whether you can locate the exits and safety equipment from memory. If you're new to this laboratory—or to this school—take some time to look around and familiarize yourself with the layout. Where is the eye-wash station? The fire blanket? The fire extinguisher? If you have any questions, ask your teacher for a quick tour.

A brief discussion of the major safety apparatus and safety procedures follows. A Safety Quiz is provided at the end of this section to test your comprehension and appreciation of this material. For additional information on safety in your particular laboratory, consult with your teacher. Your teacher may ask you to sign an agreement, indicating that you have been introduced to your school's safety regulations, and that you agree to follow them.

Protection for the Eyes

Government regulations, as well as common sense, demand the wearing of protective eyewear while you are in the laboratory. Such eyewear must be worn even if you personally are not working on an experiment. Figure 1 shows one common form of plastic **safety goggle.** Protective eyewear used in the laboratory must meet certain government regulations to be considered "safety" eyewear, and will be marked with a code number on the package and on the eyewear itself indicating the regulations the eyewear satisfies. Check eyewear carefully before purchasing to make certain it meets ANSI specifications.

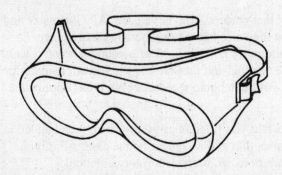

Figure 1. A typical student plastic safety goggle.

Although you may not use the particular type of goggle shown in the figure, your eyewear must include shatterproof lenses and side shields that will protect you from splashes. *Safety glasses must be worn at all times while you are in the laboratory, whether or not you are working with chemicals.*

In addition to protective goggles, an **eyewash fountain** provides eye protection in the laboratory. Should a chemical splash near your eyes, you should use the eyewash fountain before the material has a chance to run in behind your safety glasses. If the eyewash is not near your bench, wash your eyes quickly but thoroughly with water from the nearest source, and then use the eyewash. A typical eyewash fountain is indicated in Figure 2.

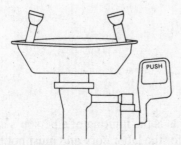

Figure 2. Laboratory emergency eyewash fountain.

The eyewash has a panic bar that enables the eyewash to be activated easily in an emergency. If you need the eyewash, don't be modest—*use it immediately*. It is critical that you protect your eyes properly.

Protection from Fire

The danger of uncontrolled fire in the chemistry laboratory is very real, since the lab typically has a fairly large number of flammable liquids in it, and open-flame gas burners are generally used for heating (see page *xix* for proper use of the gas burner). With careful attention, however, the danger of fire can be reduced considerably. Always check around the lab before lighting a gas burner to ensure that no one is pouring or using any flammable liquids. Be especially aware that the vapors of most flammable liquids are heavier than air and tend to concentrate in sinks (where they may have been poured) and at floor level. Since your laboratory may be used by other classes, always check with your instructor before beginning to use gas burners.

The method used to fight fires that occur in spite of precautions being taken depends on the size of the fire and on the substance that is burning. If only a few drops of flammable liquid have been accidentally ignited, and no other reservoir of flammable liquid is nearby, the fire can usually be put out by covering it with a beaker. This deprives the fire of oxygen and will usually extinguish the fire in a few minutes. Leave the beaker in place for several minutes to ensure that the flammable material has cooled and will not flare up again.

In the unlikely event that a larger chemical fire occurs, carbon dioxide **fire extinguishers** are available in the lab (usually mounted near one of the exits from the room). An example of a typical carbon dioxide fire extinguisher is shown in Figure 3, next page. Before activating the extinguisher, pull the metal safety ring from the handle. Direct the output from the extinguisher at the base of the flames. The carbon dioxide not only smothers the flames, it also cools the flammable material quickly. If it becomes necessary to use the fire extinguisher, be sure afterward to turn the extinguisher in at the stockroom so that it can be refilled immediately. If the carbon dioxide extinguisher does not immediately put out the fire, evacuate the laboratory and call the fire department. Carbon dioxide fire extinguishers must *not* be used on fires involving magnesium or certain other reactive metals, since carbon dioxide may react vigorously with the burning metal and make the fire worse.

Figure 3. A typical carbon dioxide
fire extinguisher. Pull the metal ring to
activate the extinguisher handle.

One of the most frightening and potentially tragic accidents is the igniting of a person's clothing. For this reason, certain types of clothing are *not appropriate* for the laboratory and must not be worn. Since sleeves are most likely to come in closest proximity to flames, any garment that has bulky or loose sleeves should not be worn in the laboratory. Certain fabrics should also be avoided; such substances as silk and certain synthetic materials may be highly flammable. Ideally, students should be asked to wear laboratory coats with tightly fitting sleeves made specifically for the chemistry laboratory. This clothing may be required by your particular college or university. Long hair also presents a clear danger if it is allowed to hang loosely in the vicinity of the flame. Long hair must be pinned back or held with a rubber band.

In the unlikely event a student's clothing or hair is ignited, his or her neighbors must take prompt action to prevent severe burns. Most laboratories have two options for extinguishing such fires: the **water shower** and the **fire blanket**. Figure 4 shows a typical laboratory emergency water shower:

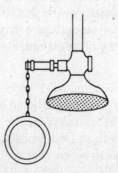

Figure 4. Laboratory emergency deluge shower.
Use the shower to extinguish clothing fires and
in the event of a large-scale chemical spill.

Generally, showers such as this are mounted near the exits from the laboratory. In the event someone's clothing or hair is on fire, *immediately* push or drag the person to the shower and pull the metal ring of the shower. Safety showers generally dump 40–50 gallons of water, which should extinguish the flames. Be aware that the showers cannot be shut off once the metal ring has been pulled. For this reason, the shower cannot be demonstrated. (But note that the showers are checked for correct operation on a regular basis.)

Figure 5 shows the other possible apparatus for extinguishing clothing fires, the **fire blanket**. The fire blanket is intended to smother flames. Since it must be operated by the person suffering the clothing fire (he or she pulls the handle of the fire blanket and wraps it around him or herself), it is therefore not the preferred method of dealing with such an event.

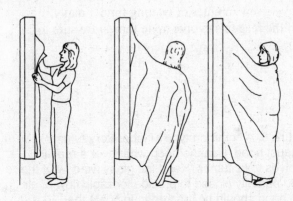

Figure 5. Fire blanket. The blanket is wrapped around the body to smother flames.

Protection from Chemical Burns

Most acids, alkalis, and oxidizing and reducing agents must be assumed to be corrosive to skin. It is impossible to avoid these substances completely, since many of them form the backbone of the study of chemistry. Usually, a material's corrosiveness is proportional to its concentration. Most of the experiments in this manual have been set up to use as dilute a mixture of reagents as possible, but this does not entirely remove the problem. Make it a personal rule to *wash your hands regularly* after using any chemical substance and to wash immediately, with plenty of water, if any chemical substance is spilled on the skin.

After working with a substance known to be particularly corrosive, you should wash your hands immediately even if you did not spill the substance. Someone else using the bottle of reagent may have spilled the substance on the side of the bottle. It is also good practice to hold a bottle of corrosive substance with a paper towel, or to wear plastic gloves, during pouring. Do not make the mistake of thinking that because an experiment calls for dilute acid, this acid cannot burn your skin. Some of the acids used in the laboratory are not volatile, and as water evaporates from a spill, the acid becomes concentrated enough to damage skin. Whenever a corrosive substance is spilled on the skin, you should inform the instructor immediately. If there is any sign whatsoever of damage to the skin, your instructor will send you to your college's health services for evaluation by a physician.

In the event of a major chemical spill in which substantial portions of the body or clothing are affected, you must use the emergency water shower. Forget about modesty, and get under the shower immediately.

Protection from Toxic Fumes

Many volatile substances may have toxic vapors. A rule of thumb for the chemistry lab is, "If you can smell it, it can probably hurt you." Some toxic fumes (such as those of ammonia) can overpower you immediately, whereas other toxic fumes are more insidious. The substance may not have that bad an odor, but its fumes can do severe damage to the respiratory system. There is absolutely no need to expose yourself to toxic fumes. All chemistry laboratories are equipped with **fume exhaust hoods**. A typical hood is indicated in Figure 6.

The exhaust hood has fans that draw vapors out of the hood and away from the user. The hood is also used when flammable solvents are required for a given procedure, since the hood will remove the vapors of such solvents from the laboratory and reduce the hazard of fire. The hood is equipped with a safety-glass window that can be used as a shield from reactions that could become too vigorous. Naturally, the number of exhaust hoods available in a particular laboratory is limited, but *never neglect to use the hood if it is called for*, merely to save a few minutes of waiting time. Finally, reagents are sometimes stored in a hood, especially if the reagents evolve toxic fumes. Be sure to return such reagents to the designated hood after use.

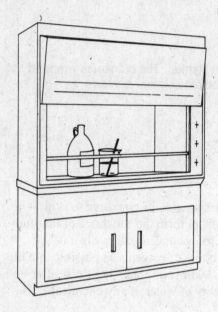

Figure 6. A common type of laboratory fume exhaust hood. Use the hood whenever a reaction involves toxic fumes. Keep the glass window of the hood partially closed to provide for rapid flow of air. The hood should be marked to indicate the maximum level the window may be raised and still provide adequate exhaust air flow.

Protection from Cuts and Simple Burns

Perhaps the most common injuries to students in the beginning chemistry laboratory are simple cuts and burns. Glass tubing and glass thermometers are used in nearly every experiment and are often not prepared or used properly. Most glass cuts occur when the glass (or thermometer) is being inserted through rubber stoppers in the construction of an apparatus. Use glycerin as a lubricant when inserting glass through rubber (several bottles of glycerine will be provided in your lab). Glycerine is a natural product of human and animal metabolism; it may be applied liberally to any piece of glass. Glycerine is water soluble, and though it is somewhat messy, it washes off easily. You should always remove glycerine before using an apparatus since the glycerine may react with the reagents to be used.

Most simple burns in the laboratory occur when a student forgets that an apparatus may be hot and touches it. Never touch an apparatus that has been heated until it has cooled for at least five minutes, or unless specific tongs for the apparatus are available.

Report any cuts or burns, no matter how apparently minor, to the instructor immediately. If there is any visible damage to the skin, you will be sent to your college's health services for immediate evaluation by a physician. What may seem like a scratch may be adversely affected by chemical reagents or may become infected; therefore, it must be attended to by trained personnel.

Proper Use of the Laboratory Burner

The laboratory burner is the most commonly used apparatus in the general chemistry laboratory, and may pose a major hazard if not used correctly and efficiently.

The typical laboratory burner is correctly called a **Tirrel burner** (though the term Bunsen burner is often used in a generic sense). A representation of a Tirrel burner is indicated in Figure 7. Compare the burner you will be using with the burner shown in the figure, and consult with your instructor if there seems to be any difference in construction. Burners from different manufacturers may differ slightly in appearance and operation from the one shown in the illustration.

Figure 7. A Tirrel burner of the sort most commonly found in student laboratories. Compare this burner with the one you will use for any differences in construction or operation. The temperature of the flame is increased by allowing air to mix with the gas being burned.

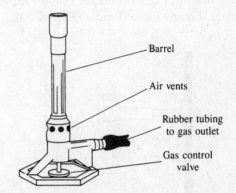

Barrel

Air vents

Rubber tubing to gas outlet

Gas control valve

Most laboratories are supplied with natural gas, which consists primarily of the hydrocarbon methane (CH_4). If your college or university is some distance from natural gas lines, your laboratory may be equipped with bottled liquefied gas, which consists mostly of the hydrocarbon propane (C_3H_8). In this case, your burner may have modifications to allow the efficient burning of propane.

A length of thin-walled rubber tubing should attach your burner to the gas main jet. If your burner has a screw-valve on the bottom for controlling the flow of gas, the valve should be closed (by turning in a right-hand direction) before you light the burner. The barrel of the burner should be rotated to close the air vents (or slide the air vent cover over the vent holes if your burner has this construction).

To light the burner, turn the gas main jet to the open position. If your burner has a screw-valve on the bottom, open this valve until you hear the hiss of gas. Without delay, use your striker or a match to light the burner. If the burner does not light on the first attempt, shut off the gas main jet, and make sure that all rubber tubing connections are tight. Then reattempt to light the burner. You may have to increase the flow of gas, using the screw-valve on the bottom of the burner.

After lighting the burner, the flame is likely to be yellow and very unstable (easily blown about by any drafts in the lab). The flame at this point is relatively cool (the gas is barely burning) and would be very inefficient in heating. To make the flame hotter and more stable, open the air vents on the barrel of the burner slowly to allow oxygen to mix with the gas before combustion. This should cause the flame's size to decrease and its color to change. A proper mixture of air and gas gives a pale blue flame, with a bright blue cone-shaped region in the center. The hottest part of the flame is directly above the tip of the bright blue cone. Whenever an item is to be heated strongly, it should be positioned directly above this bright blue cone. You should practice adjusting the flame to get the ideal pale blue flame with its blue inner cone, using the control valve on the bottom of the burner or the gas main jet.

Protection from Apparatus Accidents

An improperly constructed apparatus can create a major hazard in the laboratory, not only to the person using the apparatus, but to his or her neighbors as well. Any apparatus you set up should be constructed exactly as indicated in this manual. If you have any question as to whether you have set up the apparatus correctly, ask your instructor to check the apparatus before you begin the experiment.

Perhaps the most common apparatus accident in the lab is the tipping over of a flask or beaker while it is being heated or otherwise manipulated. All flasks should be *clamped securely* with an adjustable clamp to a ring support. This is indicated in Figure 8. Be aware that a vacuum flask is almost guaranteed to tip over during suction filtration if it is not clamped. This will result in loss of the crystals being filtered and will require that you begin the experiment again.

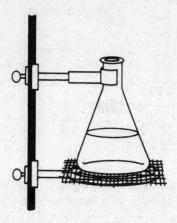

Figure 8. One method of supporting a flask. Be sure to clamp all glassware securely to a ringstand before using.

An all-too-common lab accident occurs when a liquid must be heated to boiling in a test tube. Test tubes hold only a few milliliters of liquid and require only a few seconds of heating to reach the boiling point. A test tube cannot be heated strongly in the direct full heat of the burner flame. The contents of the test tube will super-heat and blow out of the test tube like a bullet from a gun. Ideally, when a test tube requires heating, a **boiling water bath** in a beaker should be used. If this is not possible, then hold the test tube at a 45° angle a few inches above the flame and heat only *briefly*, keeping the test tube moving constantly (from top to bottom, and from side to side) through the flame during the heating. *Aim the mouth of the test tube away from yourself and your neighbors.* See Figure 9.

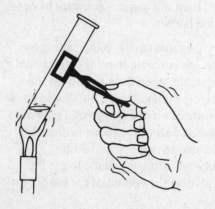

Figure 9. Method for heating a test tube containing a small quantity of liquid. Heat only for a few seconds, beginning at the *surface* of the liquid and moving downward. Keep the test tube moving through the flame. Aim the mouth of the test tube away from yourself and your neighbors.

Experiment 1

Density: A Characteristic Property

Objective

To investigate density as a typical characteristic property, a means of identification of pure substances

Concepts

Accuracy, precision, periodicity

Introduction

Density, like melting point and boiling point, is a physical property of pure substances that is always the same regardless of sample size. Because they do not depend on the amount of material being tested, such properties are called *intensive properties*. Mass and volume change with sample size, so they are known as *extensive properties*. Density, defined as the mass per unit volume, can be used as a means of identification, but is also a useful tool for deciding whether or not two objects are made of the same material—recall the famous story about how recognition of that fact led Archimedes to cry, "Eureka!"

This experiment is in two parts. In Part A, you will determine the densities of three organic liquids whose identities are known, as well as one unknown. By doing multiple trials and comparing your results for the densities of the known liquids with a list of accepted values, you will be able to gauge both the accuracy and the precision (reproducibility) of your technique. The identity of the unknown will be determined by comparing its density with the same list. A table of densities of organic liquids appears below. Water is included for comparison purposes.

Table 1–1
Densities of Some Organic Liquids (g/mL, 25 °C)

Pentane, C_5H_{12}	0.626
Hexane, C_6H_{14}	0.659
t-Butyl methyl ether, $CH_3COC(CH_3)_3$	0.741
Cyclohexane	0.779
Ethyl alcohol, CH_3CH_2OH	0.785
2-propanol, $CH_3CH(OH)CH_3$	0.786
Acetone, CH_3COCH_3	0.791
Toluene, $C_6H_5CH_3$	0.867
Ethyl acetate, $CH_3COOCH_2CH_3$	0.902
Cyclohexanol	0.962
Water	*0.997*
Dichloromethane, CH_2Cl_2	1.325
Chloroform, $CHCl_3$	1.492
Carbon tetrachloride, CCl_4	1.594
Diiodomethane, CH_2I_2	3.325

Part B involves determination of the density of irregular solids by water displacement, but it also visits one of the historically important successes of Mendeleev's periodic table. Because he noted that there were patterns to the properties of elements, Mendeleev was able to predict with fair accuracy some of the properties of previously-unknown elements. You will determine the densities of silicon and tin, both known to Mendeleev, then you will use their densities to predict the density of the then-undiscovered element, germanium, which Mendeleev called, "eka-silicon." You will compare your predicted density for germanium with the accepted value.

A Note About Accuracy and Precision

You are probably familiar with the concept of percent error and possibly even percent deviation, but the start of the year is a good time to review these ideas and to make clear the distinction between accuracy and precision. The following discussion should help in that regard.

As noted above, *precision* refers to the reproducibility of results. It is the closeness of approach of repeated measurements to a common value. By contrast, *accuracy* is the closeness of a measurement to the accepted ("true") value. To evaluate the precision of a group of measurements, you calculate the *average deviation* of the data. Begin by determining the average, or *mean*, of the measurements. You then determine the *absolute deviation* (disregard the sign) of each individual measurement from that average. The average of these absolute deviations is the *average deviation*. Consider the following set of hypothetical data.

Experiment	Density (g/mL)
1	0.98
2	0.96
3	0.99
4	0.95
5	0.97
Total	4.85

Here, the 5 is exact, so there are three significant figures (3 s.f.) in the result.

$$\text{Average (mean)} = \frac{4.85}{5} = 0.970 \text{ g/mL}$$

Experiment	Density (g/mL)	Absolute deviation
1	0.98	0.01
2	0.96	0.01
3	0.99	0.02
4	0.95	0.02
5	0.97	0.00
		0.06

Note that the average deviation has only one s.f. and it is in the hundredths place. For that reason, the mean value for density must be rounded to the hundredths place, as well.

$$\text{Average deviation} = \frac{0.06}{5} = 0.01$$

So the reported density of the liquid should be 0.97 ± 0.01 g/mL. Since 0.01 is 1% of 0.97, we can say that there is a 1% uncertainty in the result. This is a 1 significant-figure result, as you see. This percent uncertainty is often referred to as the *relative uncertainty*, since it compares the uncertainty in the measurement with its mean value.

Now, let's assume that the liquid being tested has an accepted density of 1.06 g/mL. The formula for determining percent error (% error) is:

$$\% \text{ error} = \frac{|(\text{accepted value}) - (\text{experimental value})|}{(\text{accepted value})}$$

Notice the absolute value signs surrounding the numerator of the expression for the numerator.

To determine the accuracy of the series of experiments in question, we determine the absolute value of the difference between the accepted and experimental values ($1.06 - 0.97 = 0.09$), then determine the percentage of the accepted value represented by that difference. Again following the rules governing significant figures, we get

$$\text{Percent error} = \frac{0.09}{1.06} = 0.0849056604 = 8\% \text{ error}$$

Prelaboratory Assignment

1. Read the entire experiment before coming to the laboratory.

2. Prepare a data table for Part A in your lab notebook to collect the necessary information for each of the four liquids (three known liquids and one unknown). Note that you need space to record the data for three trials with each liquid. A larger, expanded version of the one below is suggested. (The sample shows blanks for only one liquid; you will use four liquids altogether.)

3. Read the procedure description for Part B. Prepare a suitable data table for recording the measurements you are to make.

Suggested data table layout

Liquid:	Trial 1	Trial 2	Trial 3
Mass of empty vial and cap			
Mass of vial and cap plus liquid			
Mass of liquid			
Volume of liquid			

Prelaboratory Questions

1. Determine the relative error for a density experiment in which the accepted value is 0.750 g/mL, and the experimentally-obtained value is 0.735 g/mL.

2. According to one source,[1] the density of calcium is 1.55 g/cm^3, while that of barium is 3.51 g/cm^3, both at room temperature. Calculate the expected density of strontium. The accepted value for the density of strontium is 2.63 g/cm^3. What is the relative error (percent error) in the calculated density?

3. Using the accepted density for strontium given in Prelaboratory Question 2, what is the mass of exactly 1.00 cm^3 of strontium? What is the mass of 1.00 m^3 of strontium? How does this question illustrate the fact that density is an intensive property? (Hint: How many cm^3 are in one m^3?)

4. Many standard references, including the *Handbook of Chemistry and Physics*,[2] include a property of pure substances called their *specific gravity*. Specific gravity is found by dividing the density of the substance in question by the density of water. The densities of aluminum and water at 25 °C are 2.70 g/cm^3 and 0.997 g/cm^3, respectively.
    a. Determine the densities of water and aluminum in lb/in^3 (conversions: 1 lb = 453.6 g; 1 in = 2.54 cm, exactly).
    b. Show that the specific gravity of aluminum is the same, regardless of the units used for density.

---

[1] www.webelements.com

[2] David R. Lide (ed), CRC Press, 89th edition, 2008

Safety Precautions

1. Chemical splash-protective eyewear must be worn at all times in the laboratory.

2. Contact lenses should not be worn when organic vapors are present; this is especially true of plastic lenses, which absorb or dissolve in the vapors. If contacts are your only option, take extra precaution in keeping the liquids and vapors away from your eyes. Remove your goggles only when you are completely outside the laboratory.

3. Organic liquids are flammable; there must be no open flames in the same room while you are working with them.

4. Avoid breathing the vapors of organic liquids; work only in a well-ventilated space.

5. The organic liquids are toxic by ingestion. Wash your hands thoroughly with soap and water before leaving the laboratory.

Materials

Part A

Apparatus

milligram balance
small beakers, 20–30 mL or similar (4)
1 mL volumetric pipets (4)
    (graduated pipets may be substituted.)
pipet filler bulb
sample vials[3], with caps (12, if possible)
safety goggles

Reagents

ethyl acetate
hexane
acetone
unknown liquid

Part B

Apparatus

milligram balance
10-mL graduated cylinder

Reagents (in small, capped bottles)

silicon, small pieces to fit in graduate
tin, granular or small pieces; not foil
water (tap or distilled/deionized)

Procedure

Part A

The following sequence of steps is to be used for each of the four liquids. It is recommended that you do all trials for one liquid before proceeding to the next to avoid mixing containers or liquids. If partners are working individually on separate liquids, be very careful to keep your materials separate from each other.

1. Label each of three vials. Weigh each vial with its cap. The liquids are quite volatile (they will evaporate quickly) so it will be necessary to cap the vials immediately after the liquid is placed in them.

2. Obtain about 10–15 mL of the liquid to be used in a small beaker. Using the volumetric pipet and filler bulb, place exactly 1.00 mL of liquid in one vial and immediately cap it. Set it aside while you fill and cap the other two vials.

3. Weigh the capped vials with their liquid samples.

---

[3] Glass, not plastic.

4. See the section on **Disposal: Part A** for cleaning up.

5. Repeat the previous four steps, first using the other two known liquids, then with the unknown.

Part B

If you are to use the same graduated cylinder for both solids, follow the directions for **Disposal: Part B** after each use. The steps that follow are to be used for each solid sample.

6. Weigh the container of solid to the full precision of your balance ($\pm$ 0.001 g, ideally).

7. Taking care not to get droplets on the inner walls, use a wash bottle to fill the 10-mL graduated cylinder about half-way with water. Read and record the volume to $\pm$ 0.1 mL.

8. Add sufficient solid from your sample bottle to raise the water level in the graduate by at least 3.0 mL, but do not go above the 10-mL mark on the side. Be sure to add the solid carefully, to minimize splashing, as any drops of water that cling to the sides of the graduate will diminish the accuracy of your volume readings. The bottle of unused solid is weighed again. The mass of solid placed in the graduate is found by difference in the masses of bottle and contents before and after addition. The volume of solid used is found by subtracting water levels.

Disposal

Part A

1. Uncap the vials and pour the liquid into the appropriate waste container, as directed by your teacher.

2. Each of the liquids has properties different from the others, so each group of three vials needs special treatment.
    *   The vials used for acetone and ethyl acetate may be washed with soap and water, rinsed with distilled water, and allowed to air dry. Acetone is highly water-soluble, but ethyl acetate is less soluble, so be sure that there are no little beads left on the inside of the ethyl acetate vials, as this would indicate that not all of the liquid has been removed.
    *   Hexane is extremely volatile, so the vials will air dry quickly. Leave them open, with their caps, in a fume hood if available or in a well-ventilated area near your laboratory station. Once they are dry, they can be washed and rinsed as described for acetone.

3. The unknown will have its own waste container, and you have no way of knowing whether or not it is soluble in water. Consult your teacher regarding appropriate cleanup.

4. The pipettes require the same cleaning technique as the vials. Ask your teacher where they are to be placed after cleaning.

Part B

5. Do not empty your graduated cylinder directly into the sink. The solid pieces are to be collected separately in strainers, then dried and used again. After each density trial, dump the entire contents of your graduated cylinder into the appropriate strainer, using extra water if necessary to get all of the solid out. Wash and rinse the graduated cylinder. If it is to be used again, use a twisted paper towel to remove as much water from the inside walls as you can.

Analysis and Conclusions

Part A

1. For each of the four liquids, determine the individual densities of each of the three samples you ran, then calculate the mean value for the density of each liquid. Show all your calculations for

one of the liquids in your notebook. All other results can be placed in a summary table with the headings shown as follows. The average deviation is your range of experimental uncertainty. (The table shown below has space for only one liquid. Yours will have all four.)

Summary Table

Name of Liquid	Density				Individual Deviation	Average Deviation
	Trial 1	Trial 2	Trial 3	Mean		
Hexane						

2. For each of the three known liquids, report your experimental value for the density, including the uncertainty. If your accuracy was good, the accepted value will fall within the uncertainty range of your experimental value. The smaller the uncertainty range, the higher your degree of precision. For this experiment, you should be able to achieve a precision of ± 5% or better. Prepare a new table that reflects your degrees of accuracy and precision. Use the headings shown here.

Liquid	Density ± uncertainty	Accepted density	Accurate? (Y/N)	Precise? (Y/N)

3. As noted earlier, the average deviation is also considered your experimental uncertainty. In order to compare the four liquids, it is necessary to convert the actual uncertainties to percents. For each of the three known liquids, determine the percent uncertainty (consult the earlier section, "A Note about Accuracy and Precision," as needed). Now determine your *average* percent uncertainty by averaging the percentages just obtained.

Determine what the uncertainty range would be for your unknown, assuming it has the same percent uncertainty as your average for the three known liquids. Consult the list of densities that appears in the Introduction. One of those liquids is your unknown. Assuming good technique on your part, the average experimental density of your unknown should match one of the entries in the table, within the experimental uncertainty you just calculated. Identify your unknown. There is no table accompanying this question, but your work should be shown and your answers (a total of six—the uncertainties for the knowns, average percent uncertainty, uncertainty for unknown, and its identity) should be clearly identified.

4. Consider the table of densities given in the Introduction. What generalizations can you make based on what you see in that table?

Part B

5. Calculate the densities of silicon and tin, using your experimental data. The least-precise part of your data is the volume determination, which can be assumed to be ± 0.2 mL (0.1 mL for each volume reading made). Determine the percentage uncertainty this represents out of your observed volume. Thus, if the rise in volume was 3.7 mL, the percentage uncertainty is (0.2/3.7) x 100, or 5%.

6. The density of germanium (eka-silicon) is assumed to be about midway between the densities of tin and silicon. Calculate the expected density of germanium. Report this density with a percentage range equal to that found in the previous question.

7. Consult a standard reference, such as the *Handbook of Chemistry and Physics*, or an online source, such as WebElements, to find the accepted value for the density of germanium. Does the accepted value fall within your uncertainty range? Determine your percentage error using the techniques covered elsewhere in this experiment.

8. The accepted values of the densities of aluminum and indium at 20°C are 2.70 g/cm^3 and 7.31 g/cm^3, respectively. Mendeleev's prediction was that *eka-aluminum* (gallium) would have a density about halfway between these two.
   a. Based on these data, what density would Mendeleev predict for gallium?
   b. The accepted value for the density of gallium is 5.904 g/cm^3 at 29.6°C. What is the relative error (expressed as percent error) between the expected and observed values for the density of gallium?
   c. The observed melting point for gallium is 29.8°C, so the reported density of gallium was measured very near its melting point. The melting points for aluminum and indium, on the other hand, are 660°C and 157°C, respectively. Speculate as to how the density prediction might be affected by the proximity to gallium's melting point.

Experiment 2

The Formula of a Hydrate

Objective

To learn about hydrates and to determine the number of waters of hydration in a hydrate

Concepts

Hydration of ions, waters of hydration, formulas of compounds

Introduction

There is a good chance that you are sitting near several hundred pounds of hydrates as you read this, since two of the most important building materials, plaster and cement, are hydrates. Hydrates are chemical substances of definite composition formed from ionic compounds and integer or half-integer numbers of water molecules. In this experiment you will investigate some of the properties of hydrates and you will determine the number of water molecules present in a formula unit of an unknown hydrate compound. A common hydrate is bright blue copper sulfate pentahydrate, formula $CuSO_4 \cdot 5H_2O$. The dot (•) indicates that five water molecules are bound to the copper and sulfate ions. Water bound in this manner is an example of a *ligand*.

One of the most important hydrates is calcium sulfate dihydrate, $CaSO_4 \cdot 2H_2O$. The mineral gypsum is a hard, dense form of this compound. When it is heated and the two molecules of water are driven off, the *anhydrous* (water-free) calcium sulfate that remains is known as plaster of Paris. The addition of water to plaster of Paris to form the dihydrate once again is quite exothermic, producing plaster. The plaster "sets" rapidly to a highly interlocked crystalline form that has water molecules arrayed between layers of calcium and sulfate ions. The properties of plaster have been known since antiquity; plaster walls are still standing in Pompeii, and before the invention of cement, plaster was the mortar used between bricks. Another mineral form of calcium sulfate dihydrate is alabaster, used for many centuries as a sculpture medium.

Anhydrous calcium chloride, $CaCl_2$, aggressively picks up water, ultimately forming a hexahydrate. The reaction is exothermic and the resulting solution has a very low freezing point, so the primary use of the compound is for deicing roads, which it is capable of doing at temperatures down to $-51°C$. It is equally useful in the summer when it will remove moisture from the air to form a damp solid. As such it is used to control dust in highway construction. Anhydrous calcium chloride is commonly used in the laboratory as a *desiccant*, where it will remove moisture from air (in a closed vessel called a desiccator) or from gases that flow through particles of the solid. It also has the property of removing water from organic liquids such as diethyl ether, which can dissolve about 8% of its weight in water.

Copper sulfate pentahydrate is blue while the anhydrous salt is white. Cobalt chloride in moist air is a hexahydrate, $CoCl_2 \cdot 6 H_2O$, which is red, while in dry, cool air it is the blue anhydrous salt. At moderate humidity levels it is present as the purple dihydrate, $CoCl_2 \cdot 2H_2O$, so it can serve as an indicator of relative humidity. It is incorporated, for example, with the desiccant silica gel found in the packaging of electronic equipment; when the desiccant turns pink it needs to be replaced or reactivated by heating.

Some hydrates lose water at room temperature and normal humidity; they are said to *effloresce* (or, they are efflorescent). Other compounds, such as calcium chloride and sodium hydroxide, pick up so much moisture from the air that they dissolve in the resulting liquid. These substances *deliquesce*; they are *deliquescent*.

A very large class of organic compounds is called carbohydrates. This might seem to imply that they are hydrates of carbon; that misconception arose in the middle of the 18th century when only the empirical formulas, $[C(H_2O)_n]$, of many sugars were known. The empirical formula for glucose, $C_6H_{12}O_6$, seems as if it could be rewritten as $C_6(H_2O)_6$, but this sugar is not carbon hexahydrate. True hydrate formation is completely reversible; this is not the case with carbohydrates. But they can be partially dehydrated; that is, some of the material can be driven off as water as a result of heating. When a sugar is heated it will lose the elements of water, but in the process will decompose irreversibly. Partial dehydration of sucrose, $C_{12}H_{22}O_{11}$, leads to taffy, caramel, and finally to the dark brown substance from which peanut brittle is made.

Prelaboratory Assignment

1. Read the entire experiment before coming to the laboratory.

2. Prepare a data table for recording the results of your tests for Part A, and another for recording the masses in Part B.

Prelaboratory Questions

1. Define the term *hydrate* (without copying words from the Introduction) and explain the function of the dot (•) in the formulas of hydrates. How is the dot treated when you are calculating the molar mass of a hydrate?

2. What is the meaning of the term, *anhydrous*?

3. If the unknown hydrate in Part B is not heated sufficiently to drive off all of the waters of hydration, what will be the effect on the calculation of the number of waters of hydration?

Safety Precautions

1. Chemical splash-protective eyewear must be worn at all times in the laboratory.

2. Cobalt compounds are moderately toxic. Wash your hands thoroughly with soap and water before leaving the laboratory.

3. Hot and cold glassware look alike. Be careful handling the test tubes and watch glasses in this experiment.

Materials

Apparatus

small hot plate
10 x 75-mm culture tubes (11)
wire test tube clamp
glass stirring rod
thin-stem transfer pipet
Bunsen burner
wire screen with ceramic center
   (for cooling tubes)

Reagents

calcium sulfate
cobalt(II) chloride
copper(II) chloride
copper(II) sulfate
nickel(II) chloride
potassium carbonate
potassium chloride
sucrose (table sugar)
unknown hydrate

Procedure

Part A

1. Turn on the hotplate; use the "low" setting. Place a small amount of each of the eight known solids into seven separate 10 x 75-mm culture tubes (use only enough to cover the bottom of the tube). Crush the solids to a fine powder with a glass stirring rod if necessary. Heat the bottom of each tube on a hot plate or in a burner flame and observe any changes. If the compound loses water on heating, moisture should collect on the upper portion of the tube. This is an indication the compound you are testing is a hydrate. Note the appearance (especially color) of the solid after heating. Record which tubes showed evidence of dehydration and specify the evidence that you saw.

2. **After the tubes cool**, add about a milliliter of water to each one using a thin-stem pipet, stir, and observe what happens. If the substance is a hydrate it should dissolve and give a solution close in color to the original hydrated salt.

Part B

3. After marking them for identification, carefully weigh (±0.001g) each of your three remaining tubes. Add about 0.4 g of an unknown hydrate into each tube and weigh them again, to the same precision. The masses of the three samples need not be equal, but they should be recorded to the full precision of the balance. Crush the material to a fine powder with a glass rod.

4. Using a test tube clamp, hold the tubes one at a time in the flame of a small Bunsen burner. Heat for 15 minutes or longer. After the first 8–10 minutes, move the tube around in the flame so that any drops of water that may collect on the upper parts of the tubes are heated to dryness.

5. Allow the tubes to cool to room temperature and weigh them carefully, recording the mass of each. Be sure you know which tube is which, since you will need to know the amount by which the mass changed in each one. While a desiccator is recommended for cooling the tubes, most of the solids used as unknowns will not rehydrate quickly, so briefly cooling in open air should not affect results.

Disposal

1. All of the substances used in this experiment except cobalt chloride are relatively harmless and can be flushed down the drain with water. All cobalt chloride samples should be placed in the receptacle provided for recycling or disposal.

2. Clean all glassware (tubes, stirring rods) and return them to their proper locations.

Analysis and Conclusions

1. Of the seven solids tested in Part A, identify the ones that were hydrates, citing evidence for your choices. Then explain how you know that the others were not hydrates.

2. For each of your three tubes from Part B:
   a. Determine the mass of each sample and the mass of water lost during heating.
   b. Determine the percentage of water (by mass) in the original hydrated sample in each tube.

3. You will be provided with the name and/or formula of the anhydrous form of the compound you used for Part B. Determine the molar mass of the compound, then:
   a. Determine the number of moles of water that were lost during heating.
   b. Determine the number of moles of anhydrous compound that were left in the tube after heating.

    c. Determine the ratio, moles of water per mole of anhydrous solid, for each of your three samples.

4. Assuming that the number of waters of hydration must be a whole number:

    a. What is the nearest whole-number value for the ratio of moles of water to moles of salt?

    b. Write the formula of the hydrate in the form $X \cdot Y\,H_2O$, where X represents the formula for the salt and Y is the number of waters of hydration.

5. Suggest at least two reasonable explanations for any non-whole-number experimental ratios that you reported in Question **3c**, above.

6. In this experiment, you used hydrates that included two compounds, both containing copper(II) ions: copper(II) chloride, $CuCl_2$, and copper(II) sulfate, $CuSO_4$.

    a. What color were the two hydrated copper compounds?

    b. What color were the anhydrous forms of these two compounds?

    c. Sodium chloride and potassium chloride are not hydrates; what color are they?

    d. If both copper(II) compounds were blue (albeit of different shades), and if dehydrated compounds containing chloride ions are white, speculate as to whether the water molecules in hydrated compounds are more likely bonded to the cation or the anion in each case, and defend your answer.

Experiment 3

Gravimetric Analysis of a Sulfate Mixture

Objective

To determine the relative percentages of sodium and potassium sulfates in an unknown mixture

Concepts

Gravimetric analysis, stoichiometry, mole ratios

Introduction

In this experiment you will be given a sample that contains sulfate ion. It is a mixture of two compounds, sodium sulfate and potassium sulfate, both anhydrous salts. Your first task is to determine the total number of moles of sulfate ion in the original mixture. From that quantity and using the total mass of your sample and the molar masses of the two components of the mixture, you will be able to determine the composition of the sulfate mixture.

This requires careful technique. Your results will be evaluated, in part, on how close you come to the actual composition of the mixture. The sulfate mixture will dissolve in water. When an aqueous solution of barium chloride is added to the solution, insoluble barium sulfate will precipitate from the solution.

$$SO_4^{2-}(aq) + Ba^{2+}(aq) \rightarrow BaSO_4(s) \tag{3-1}$$

The precipitate is collected by centrifugation, washed carefully, dried, and weighed. This experiment is an example of *gravimetric analysis*. You can expect to spend about an hour on the first day, plus short periods of time on one or more successive days, perhaps while another experiment is in progress.

Prelaboratory Assignment

1. Read the entire experiment before coming to the laboratory.

2. Prepare a data table for recording masses and descriptive observations.

Prelaboratory Questions

1. Write the balanced molecular and complete-ionic equation for the reaction between barium chloride and potassium sulfate in aqueous solution to form barium sulfate. Show that the net-ionic equation for this reaction is the same as was given above.

2. Suggest a reason why it is desirable to use an excess of barium ion in the precipitation.

3. A sample of an unknown sulfate compound has a mass of 0.1000g. Addition of excess barium chloride solution to the sample forms a barium sulfate precipitate of mass 0.0676g. What is the mass percent of sulfate ion in the unknown compound?

4. Hydrated calcium sulfate, $CaSO_4$, contains of 55.8% sulfate ion, by mass. Calculate the number of waters of hydration that are present in the hydrate. Write the correct formula for the hydrate.

Safety Precautions

1. Chemical splash-protective eyewear must be worn at all times in the laboratory.

2. Hydrochloric acid is corrosive to skin and clothing.

3. Barium compounds are toxic. Wash thoroughly with soap and water before leaving the laboratory.

Materials

Apparatus

milligram balance
100-mm test tube
small hotplate
desiccator
centrifuge

Reagents

1.0 M HCl
1.0 M BaCl$_2$

Procedure

For the most precise results, duplicate determinations should be carried out, each following the sequence of steps given below. The sample mass should be in the range of 100–150 mg if a balance with milligram sensitivity is used, or 50–100 mg if an analytical balance is available.

Note: If you were given a <u>numbered</u> unknown sample, be sure to record the number in your notebook.

1. Determine the mass of a clean, dry 100-mm test tube. Place a small amount of the unknown (about the volume equivalent of one grain of rice) in the tube, then reweigh the tube and contents. Add about 1 mL of distilled water to dissolve the sample, gently warming the tube on a hot plate or *carefully* in a burner flame if necessary. If the mixture is heated too strongly, it may "bump" and some of the liquid may be lost. Some solids may require more water, but be careful not to fill the tube beyond about 1/3 full. The sample must be completely dissolved before proceeding.

2. Add 2 drops of 1 M HCl to the tube and shake gently. Follow this with 0.5–1.0 mL of 1.0 M BaCl$_2$ added dropwise, with gentle shaking after each 2–3 drops. Take care not to get barium chloride on your skin; if you do, wash it off with soap and water. Warm the tube and contents on a hotplate for 2–3 minutes to aid coagulation of the precipitate. Do not boil.

3. Remove the tube from the heat, allow it to cool, then centrifuge for 30 seconds. Without disturbing the solid on the bottom of the test tube, add one more drop of the barium chloride solution. If no new cloudiness appears, proceed with the washing of the precipitate (step 4). If cloudiness is observed, add five more drops of the BaCl$_2$, then heat, centrifuge, and test again with barium chloride; continue in this fashion until addition of barium chloride does not cause further cloudiness.

4. Decant and discard the clear supernatant solution above the barium sulfate precipitate, being careful not to lose any solid. A microtip transfer pipet or Pasteur pipet is useful for this purpose. Add about 10 drops of ice-cold distilled water to the solid in the tube, then shake the tube and contents until all of the precipitate is suspended in the water (it will not dissolve). Centrifuge the suspension and again discard the clear, colorless supernatant, being careful not to lose any of the white solid. Repeat the ice-water rinse, centrifuging, and decanting twice more, followed by a final rinsing with acetone.

5. Dry the test tube and precipitate first on a steam bath to drive off most of the acetone and then in a 105–110°C oven for at least one hour, preferably overnight.

6. Remove the tube from the oven and allow it to cool for a minimum of 30 minutes in a desiccator. Determine the mass of the tube and contents. Return the tube to the oven for at least an hour, cool in the desiccator once more, then reweigh it. If the mass agrees within experimental error (± 0.5% of the precipitate mass) with the previous value, the experiment is completed. If not, continue the cycle of oven-drying, cooling, and weighing until a constant mass is obtained.

Disposal

1. Barium sulfate, like barium chloride, is toxic by ingestion. Transfer your solid product to an appropriate container for removal as hazardous waste. Small amounts of barium ion were washed into the effluent stream during the decanting and rinsing portions of the procedure; this is unavoidable, but the amounts are below the parts-per-trillion level, so present no significant hazard to the environment.

2. Wash all glassware immediately after use and return it to its proper location.

Processing the Data

1. Determine each of the following, showing appropriate calculations to support your results. If you did two or more trials, as was suggested, you need only show calculations for one of the trials, with results for all presented in the form of a table, with separate columns for each sample.
    - Mass of original sulfate sample

    - Mass and moles of barium sulfate produced

    - Moles and mass of sulfate ion present in unknown sample

    - Mass percent of sulfate ion in unknown

2. The unknown that you used was a mixture of potassium sulfate, K_2SO_4, and sodium sulfate, Na_2SO_4. Here's what you know:
    - The total number of moles of barium sulfate equals the number of moles of sulfate ion in the original sample, which, in turn, must equal the combined moles of K_2SO_4 and Na_2SO_4.

    - The total mass of the original sample must be the combined masses of K_2SO_4 and Na_2SO_4.

    - The mass of K_2SO_4 is found by multiplying the number of moles of K_2SO_4 by the molar mass of K_2SO_4; likewise, the mass of Na_2SO_4 is found by multiplying the number of moles of Na_2SO_4 by the molar mass of Na_2SO_4.

    - The number moles of Na_2SO_4 must be the difference between the total moles of sulfate and the number of moles of K_2SO_4 in the original sample.

    Given this information it is a simple matter of algebra to determine the masses of K_2SO_4 and Na_2SO_4 that were in the original sample, and from those you can establish the mass percent composition of the sample mixture. Thus, if the number of moles of barium sulfate recovered is, say, 7.50×10^{-4} mol, and if the number of moles of K_2SO_4 is represented by x, then the number of moles of Na_2SO_4 would be $(7.50 \times 10^{-4} - x)$. If you carried out multiple trials, you need only show the actual calculations for one trial; simply report the masses of K_2SO_4 and Na_2SO_4, and the percentage composition of the mixture for each additional trial.

Analysis and Conclusions

1. Suggest explanations for each of the following parts of the procedure.
    a. The first three rinsings of the product specified the use of distilled water that was ice-cold, rather than room temperature.
    b. Acetone is used for the final rinse.

2. What would be the effect on your determination of the mass of barium sulfate in each of the following cases? For each one, you are to decide whether the reported mass of $BaSO_4$ would be too high, too low, or unaffected. Explain the reasoning behind your choice.
    a. Too little barium chloride solution was used.
    b. The sample was not thoroughly dried.
    c. The tube and contents were not cool before the final weighing.

3. The purpose of adding hydrochloric acid in Part B is to remove any carbonate ions that might be present in the unknown, so that barium carbonate will not precipitate along with the sulfate. Write the net-ionic equation for the reaction between protons (hydrogen ions) in solution and dissolved carbonate ions. What effect on your sulfate percentage could result if the addition of acid were omitted? Explain.

4. What effect on your sulfate percentage could result if the addition of acid were omitted? Explain.

5. **Error analysis:** Discuss experimental errors and identify those portions of the procedure where extra care is needed to ensure satisfactory results.

Experiment 4

The Concentration of Acetic Acid in Vinegar

Objective

To determine the concentration of acetic acid in vinegar

Concepts

Primary standards, use of volumetric glassware, acid-base titrations

Introduction

This experiment is in two parts: Part A involves standardization of an unknown sodium hydroxide solution and part of your pre-lab assignment is to calculate the concentrations of solutions needed for the experiment to work. In Part B, you will use the sodium hydroxide to determine the strength of commercial vinegar.

It is impossible to prepare solutions of most solutes in accurately-known concentrations. For example, sodium hydroxide tends to absorb both water and carbon dioxide from the air. The former affects the mass of material, although it does not change it chemically; the latter reacts with NaOH, forming, in turn, bicarbonate and carbonate ions. For that reason, sodium hydroxide is prepared in approximately the concentration desired, then standardized against a *primary standard*. A primary standard is a substance that is obtainable in high purity and whose mass can be measured with high precision. The primary standard usually chosen for strong base solutions is potassium hydrogen phthalate, or KHP, for short. Figure 4-1 shows the structure of KHP. In this short-hand form, the corners of the hexagon are understood to be occupied by carbon atoms. The four carbon atoms that do not have carboxyl groups attached each have one hydrogen atom to complete their valence configuration.

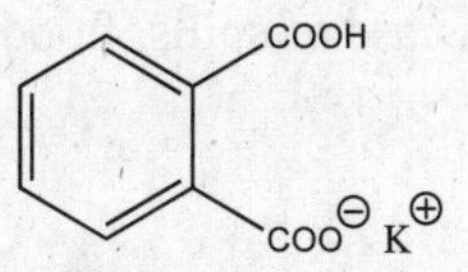

The potassium ion has replaced one of the acidic hydrogen atoms on the phthalic acid molecule. In the standardization step, the other acidic hydrogen (H on COOH) reacts with hydroxide ion.

Figure 4-1

You will be provided with a sodium hydroxide solution with a molar concentration of approximately 0.1 M. You will *standardize* the solution against potassium acid phthalate primary standard to get a more precise value for its concentration, in units of moles of NaOH per gram of sodium hydroxide solution. If possible, all masses should be determined using an analytical balance so that the concentrations will have three significant-figure precision.

In Part B you will use the standardized sodium hydroxide solution to determine the concentration of acetic acid in ordinary household vinegar. Since the concentration of acetic acid is in the range 0.8–1.0 M, it will be necessary to dilute the vinegar tenfold; you will use volumetric glassware for this purpose. The diluted vinegar will be titrated with the standard NaOH to establish the concentration of the diluted acid, again in moles of acetic acid per gram of diluted vinegar. Using your dilution data, you will calculate the density of the diluted vinegar, and then use the density to determine the mass percent of acetic acid in both the diluted and the full-strength vinegar solutions.

Prelaboratory Assignment

Read the entire experiment before you begin. Prepare a data table for Part A that includes spaces for recording the mass of KHP used, the initial and final masses of the NaOH pipet, and the mass of NaOH used. Set your table up for three trials, but leave space in case one or more additional trials is needed. (See the instructions following step 4.)

Prelaboratory Questions

1. Pure acetic acid is a liquid, with density 1.0492 g/mL at 25°C. An aqueous solution that is 0.1000 molar (0.1000 M) in acetic acid contains 6.0053 g of solute per liter of solution. Calculate: (a) the respective volumes of acetic acid and water needed to make a total volume of 1.000 L, and (b) the concentration of the solution in mol $HC_2H_3O_2$/gram of solution. At 25°C, the density of pure water is 0.9969 g/mL.

2. What mass of 1.00×10^{-1} M NaOH solution will be needed to titrate 25.0 mg of KHP? Assume a density of 1.04 g/mL for the NaOH solution.

3. Using the information from question 2, convert the concentration given for the NaOH to moles of solute per gram of solution.

4. Commercial vinegar is approximately 5% acetic acid by mass. Assuming a density of 1.006 g/mL, calculate the molar concentration of acetic acid in vinegar. If 1.00 g of this solution is to be neutralized by 0.10 M NaOH, what volume of base will be required? A microtip pipet holds about 3.5 grams of solution; will one pipet-full of base be enough to titrate 1.00 g of full-strength vinegar? Show calculations to defend your answer.

Safety Precautions

1. Chemical splash-protective eyewear must be worn at all times in the laboratory.

2. Sodium hydroxide is caustic and particularly dangerous to the eyes. In case of spills, flood the affected area with water for 5 minutes.

Materials

Apparatus

balance, analytical or milligram
10- or 25-mL Erlenmeyer flasks
pipets, microtip (2) for NaOH and vinegar
volumetric flask, 10- or 25-mL
volumetric or Mohr pipet, 1.0 mL or 2.5 mL

Reagents

sodium hydroxide, NaOH(aq), ~0.1 M
potassium hydrogen phthalate (KHP), solid
distilled water, in wash bottle
phenolphthalein, 0.5% (alcohol)
commercial "white" vinegar

Note: The potassium hydrogen phthalate primary standard must be dried in a 110°C oven for at least two hours before use. The dried solid acid is transferred to a desiccator to cool for a minimum of one hour, or until it is needed.

Procedure

Part A: Standardization of Sodium Hydroxide by Potassium Hydrogen Phthalate

1. Using an analytical balance if available, place between 20 and 25 mg (± 0.1 mg) of primary standard KHP in each of three 10-mL Erlenmeyer flasks. Add about 1–1.5 mL of distilled water to each flask and swirl to dissolve the solid acid, followed by one drop of 0.5% phenolphthalein indicator solution.

2. Fill a microtip pipet with the NaOH that is to be standardized. Wipe the tip of the pipet dry, and then determine the mass of pipet and contents (± 0.1 mg).

3. Titrate the first KHP sample by adding a few drops at a time of the NaOH and swirling after each addition. Continue in this fashion until you achieve a faint pink color that persists throughout the solution for at least 30 seconds. Record the final mass of your NaOH pipet.

4. Repeat Steps 2 and 3 with each of your other two KHP samples, refilling and reweighing the NaOH pipet between trials as necessary.

   Precision check: Calculate the mass of NaOH solution used per gram of KHP for each of the three trials. Determine the mean value for the ratio, then determine the relative deviation. If that relative deviation exceeds 5% of the mean, do one or more additional trials until you have three that show less than 5% deviation.

Part B: Determination of the Mass Percent of Acetic Acid in Commercial Vinegar

5. **Dilution of commercial vinegar:** Weigh a clean, dry 10-mL volumetric flask, then use a volumetric pipet to transfer exactly 1.00 mL of a commercial vinegar product to the flask. Weigh the flask and contents once again, and then use distilled water to bring the volume of solution in the flask up to exactly 10.00 mL; then weigh the flask and contents to the nearest 0.1 mg (if possible). Your teacher will show you how to ensure that the diluted vinegar solution is thoroughly mixed. Weigh the flask and contents once again.

6. You will now use the standardized solution of sodium hydroxide to titrate three (at least) samples of the diluted vinegar. Following the procedure of Part A, prepare three fresh sample vessels, each containing 1.0–1.5 gram of the diluted vinegar solution in place of the potassium acid phthalate. As before, add phenolphthalein to all three and titrate each with the sodium hydroxide, which you standardized in Part A.

   Precision check: Calculate the mass of NaOH solution used per gram of diluted vinegar for each of the three trials. Determine the mean value for the ratio, then determine the relative deviation. If that relative deviation exceeds 5% of the mean, do one or more additional trials until you have three that show less than 5% deviation.

Disposal

The contents of the titration vessels can be safely rinsed down the drain with water, as can leftover diluted vinegar. Unused NaOH must first be neutralized. If you have approximately equal volumes of NaOH and dilute vinegar, it is safe to combine them and rinse down the drain. For excess NaOH, add a few drops of phenolphthalein, then add vinegar until the pink color appears.

Analysis and Conclusions

1. Use your data from Part A to determine the concentration of the sodium hydroxide solution in mol NaOH/g solution. Show your work for one trial and report the average concentration and average deviation.

2. Using the average value for the concentration of NaOH, determine the number of moles of acetic acid in each sample of the diluted vinegar that you titrated in Part B. Convert these to moles of acetic acid per gram of dilute vinegar by dividing the number of moles of acetic acid by the mass or the respective samples. As before, calculate individual values for each trial, then report an average value and average deviation.

3. Based on your average value for the number of moles of acetic acid per gram of diluted vinegar and using the data from the dilution, determine:
   a. The density of the diluted vinegar
   b. The mass percent of acetic acid in the original (undiluted) vinegar solution

4. The Introduction describes two successive side-reactions that can change the make-up of sodium hydroxide. Write balanced equations showing: (a) the reaction between carbon dioxide and hydroxide ions to form bicarbonate ions, and (b) the further reaction between bicarbonate and excess hydroxide to form carbonate ions. Does either of the two processes represent an acid-base reaction according to the Bronsted-Lowry system? Discuss.

5. In preparing a sodium hydroxide solution that is to be used for quantitative work, the usual technique is to boil the water first to drive off dissolved CO_2. Based on the equilibria you wrote in response to Question 4, what effect (if any) would the presence of carbonates or bicarbonates have on the ability of the solution to neutralize hydronium ions? Explain.

6. Also mentioned in the Introduction is the fact that sodium hydroxide aggressively absorbs water vapor from the air. What effect would this have on the concentration of a solution prepared by dissolving 40.00 grams of solid sodium hydroxide in water to make 1.000 L of solution? Be very specific in your response.

7. At room temperature, the molar solubility of carbon dioxide in water is about 0.033 M. Would you expect the solubility of carbon dioxide in a solution containing sodium hydroxide to be greater or less than 0.033 mol/L? Explain using the equations for the reaction(s) involved.

8. Use appropriate equations to explain why a white crust will sometimes form when sodium hydroxide that has been exposed to air is dissolved in "hard" tap water. (Hint: "hard" water contains calcium and/or magnesium ions. Consider the solubility rules.)

9. Write balanced net-ionic equations for: (a) the reaction between hydroxide ions and hydrogen phthalate ions, $HC_4H_8O_4^-$, with the first H being the acidic hydrogen; and (b) the reaction between (molecular) acetic acid and hydroxide ions. (See Figure 4-1.)

Experiment 5

Oxidation and Reduction

Objective

To learn about some of the types of reactions that are driven by electron transfer

Concepts

Oxidation and reduction, oxidizing and reducing agents, half-reactions

Introduction

Many reactions involve transfer of electrons from one atom or ion to another. Such processes are known as *oxidations* (for electron loss) and *reductions* (for electron gain). Since they always occur together, they are referred to collectively as oxidation-reduction reactions, or simply as "*redox reactions*."

If an atom is oxidized (loses electrons), those electrons must be transferred to some other atom or ion; the atom or ion that takes the electrons is called the *oxidizing agent*. This name suggests that the receiver of the electrons caused the oxidation to occur. So the species that is reduced (gains electrons) is the oxidizing agent. Similarly, the species that is oxidized is called a *reducing agent* because it provided the electrons that caused the other atom or ion to become reduced.

In this experiment, you will investigate some of the types of reactions for which electron transfer is the driving force. You have met many of these before and you may know them under other names. The first three parts will be carried out in a 96-well test plate, but Part D involves reagents that can attack the plastic, so you will use small test tubes, beakers, or flasks for the final steps.

Prelaboratory Assignment

Read the entire experiment before you begin.

Prelaboratory Questions

1. **a.** What are the most common ionic charges for the elements shown?
   Aluminum   Oxygen
   b. Complete the following oxidation or reduction half-reactions in your notebook, showing aluminum and oxygen gas forming the ions you identified in 1a.
   (*i*) $Al(s) \rightarrow$ _____ + _____
   (*ii*) $O_2(g) +$ _____ $\rightarrow$ 2 _____
   c. Identify each of the reaction equations as being either an oxidation or a reduction.

2. Write the balanced equation for the reaction between aluminum metal and oxygen gas to form aluminum oxide.

3. Identify each of the following processes as an example of oxidation, reduction, or both.
   a. Chlorine gas becomes chloride ion.
   b. Sodium metal becomes sodium ions.
   c. Iron rusts.
   d. Hydrogen peroxide breaks down into water and oxygen gas. (Hint: the oxygen in hydrogen peroxide, H_2O_2, has an oxidation state of 1–.)
   e. Household bleach removes a stain from an article of clothing.

4. Steps 6 and 7 direct you to very gently note the odors produced by reactions. Describe the correct technique for doing this when the odor being tested may be unpleasant, toxic, or both.

Safety Precautions

1. Chemical splash-protective eyewear must be worn at all times in the laboratory.

2. Hydrochloric, sulfuric, and oxalic acids are corrosive to skin and clothing.

3. Wipe up all spills immediately using large quantities of water.

4. Small quantities of gaseous halogens may be generated. Work in a well-ventilated area.

Materials

Apparatus

24-well test plates (2; one to hold pipets)
wash bottle
forceps or tweezers
toothpicks as stirring rods
small test tubes (75-mm or similar) (5)

Solid Reagents

magnesium foil (small pieces)
copper foil (small pieces)
zinc foil (small pieces)

Reagent Solutions

In microtip pipettes

0.50 M hydrochloric acid, HCl(aq)
0.50 M cupric nitrate, $Cu(NO_3)_2$(aq)
1.0 M zinc nitrate, $Zn(NO_3)_2$(aq)
0.10 M potassium permanganate, $KMnO_4$
0.10 M ferric chloride, $FeCl_3$(aq)
0.10 M ferrous sulfate, $FeSO_4$(aq)

In thin-stem pipettes

0.10 M ammonium *meta*-vanadate, NH_4VO_3
3% hydrogen peroxide, H_2O_2
3 M sulfuric acid, H_2SO_4(aq)
0.1 M oxalic acid, $H_2C_2O_4$
0.5 M sodium sulfite, Na_2SO_3(aq)
bleach, 5.25% sodium hypochlorite, NaOCl(aq)

Procedure

Part A

1. Place 10 drops of 0.50 M HCl in a cell of your test plate. Add a small piece of magnesium then observe and record what happens as the reaction proceeds.

Part B

2. Add 10 drops of 0.50 M copper nitrate, $Cu(NO_3)_2$, to one well of your test plate and add a small piece of zinc metal. Record your observations, both of the appearance of the metal and of the solution color. Changes may not happen right away.

3. Put 10 drops of 0.50 M zinc nitrate, $Zn(NO_3)_2$, in a different well of your test plate. Add a small piece of copper metal. Observe and record any reactions that take place, including solution color and changes at the surface of the metal.

Part C

4. Place 10 drops of 0.1 M iron(III) chloride (a source of Fe^{3+} ion) in one well of your test plate and 10 drops of iron(II) sulfate (a source of Fe^{2+} ion) in another well. Add a single drop of 0.1 M potassium permanganate, $KMnO_4$, to each well. One of the wells will show a change in the color of the $KMnO_4$; the other will not. Note which iron ion reacts with (decolorizes) the $KMnO_4$.

5. To the well from step 4 in which the purple color disappeared, continue adding potassium permanganate, one drop at a time and stirring after each drop, until the purple color of the permanganate ion no longer fades. Record the number of drops needed to complete the reaction.

Part D   **Note:**   The reagents for this part of the experiment will attack the plastic well plate, so small glass vessels will be used.

For many transition metals, more than one possible cation can be formed. When an atom or ion changes its charge, we say it has undergone a change in oxidation state. Since these oxidation state changes are often accompanied by a change in the color the metal ion gives to aqueous solutions, it is a simple matter to tell when an oxidation or reduction of the metal occurs.

6. Manganese; the 7+ oxidation state, in potassium permanganate, $KMnO_4$.

    a. Put 10 drops of hydrogen peroxide antiseptic in a 10- or 20-mL beaker or Erlenmeyer flask. Add one drop of 3 M H_2SO_4 and swirl the vessel gently to mix the reagents. Now add a single drop of potassium permanganate solution, $KMnO_4$(aq), and observe the changes that take place. (Hint: you should see two changes, only one of which involves the color of the $KMnO_4$.)

    b. Repeat the previous step, but omit the sulfuric acid.

    c. Repeat step 6a but this time use 0.1 M oxalic acid solution, $H_2C_2O_4$, in place of the hydrogen peroxide and sulfuric acid. If no changes are evident after 1 minute, try warming the vessel on a hot plate.

7. Vanadium in the 4+ and 5+ oxidation states.

    a. Place about 1 mL of ammonium vanadate solution in a small (10- or 25-mL) beaker or Erlenmeyer flask. The color you see is due to vanadium in the 5+ state.[1] Add an equal volume of sodium sulfite solution and swirl the flask. If no change occurs within 30 seconds heat the flask gently on the hot plate. Note and record the color of the solution, which now contains vanadium in the 4+ state.[2] **Gently** note the odor coming from the flask; it isn't pleasant.

    b. Allow the flask to cool, then add 2–3 mL of bleach, an aqueous solution of sodium hypochlorite, NaOCl. Observe and record any changes. Again, there will be a noticeable odor, but do not smell the contents directly. Chlorine gas is generated, and it is quite toxic.

Disposal

1. Remove any bits of unreacted metal that may remain in your test plate to the appropriate waste container.

2. To the tubes from **Part D**, step 7, add about 1 mL of 0.5 M sodium sulfite solution, Na_2SO_3, to convert any remaining molecular chlorine to chloride ions.

3. Flush remaining solutions down the drain with large amounts of water. While some of the solutes are potential hazards and others are quite acidic, the dilution provided by a running stream of water will bring the concentrations to acceptable levels.

4. Return the pipettes and unused solutions to their proper place. Do not empty them into the sink.

---

[1] Specifically, it is the dioxovanadium ion, VO_2^+.
[2] This ion is the vanadyl ion, VO^{2+}. Be sure to note the difference in their formulas.

AP Experimental Chemistry

Analysis and Conclusions

The following list shows six equations that you will need in order to answer the questions for Parts A–C. They are called half-reactions because each shows only half of an oxidation-reduction process. Each is written twice, first as reductions, then reversed to become oxidations. Notice that atoms are not always conserved in these half-reactions. (e^- = electron(s).)

Reductions	Oxidations
$Zn^{2+} + 2e^- \rightarrow Zn$	$Zn \rightarrow Zn^{2+} + 2e^-$
$Cu^{2+} + 2e^- \rightarrow Cu$	$Cu \rightarrow Cu^{2+} + 2e^-$
$Mg^{2+} + 2e^- \rightarrow Mg$	$Mg \rightarrow Mg^{2+} + 2e^-$
$Fe^{3+} + e^- \rightarrow Fe^{2+}$	$Fe^{2+} \rightarrow Fe^{3+} + e^-$
$2H^+ + 2e^- \rightarrow H_2$	$H_2 \rightarrow 2H^+ + 2e^-$
$Cl_2 + 2e^- \rightarrow 2Cl^-$	$2Cl^- \rightarrow Cl_2 + 2e^-$
$SO_4^{2-} + 2e^- \rightarrow SO_3^{2-}$	$SO_3^{2-} \rightarrow SO_4^{2-} + 2e^-$
$VO_2^+ + e^- \rightarrow VO^{2+}$	$VO^{2+} \rightarrow VO_2^+ + e^-$
$OCl^- + e^- \rightarrow Cl_2$	$Cl_2 \rightarrow OCl^- + e^-$

Part A

1. The only possible states for magnesium are the neutral element (zero charge) and the dipositive cation, Mg^{2+}.
   a. With which did you begin?
   b. What was the oxidation state of magnesium after it had reacted with HCl?
   c. Was magnesium oxidized or reduced? Explain.
   d. Write the half-reaction showing the change for magnesium.

2. The hydrochloric acid solution contains H^+ ions and Cl^- ions. Consult the list of half-reactions given above to decide what gas was bubbling out of the reaction. (Hint: Recall that you need one oxidation and one reduction taking place in order to have a complete system, so this gas must form as a result of the choice you did not select in 1c, above.) Write the equation for the half-reaction resulting in the evolution of the gas you select.

3. Combine your half-reactions from questions 1 and 2, above, to write the net-ionic equation for the complete reaction. (Chemical equations such as these half-reactions may be combined by addition, just as you would do with algebraic equations.)

Part B

4. Consider the two wells used for zinc and copper.
   a. What evidence of reaction did you see in each case, if any?
   b. One of the following equations represents the reaction that occurred; select the correct one and justify your choice.
   $$Cu + Zn^{2+} \rightarrow Cu^{2+} + Zn \qquad \text{or} \qquad Cu^{2+} + Zn \rightarrow Cu + Zn^{2+}$$
   c. For the reaction equation you selected in 4b, identify each of the following:
   (*i*) the species that is reduced: (*ii*) the species that is oxidized:
   (*iii*) the reducing agent: (*iv*) the oxidizing agent:

Part C

5. a. In which well was the color of permanganate ion lost? That is, which test reagent, Fe^{2+} or Fe^{3+}, caused the purple color to fade?
   b. The permanganate and iron solutions were both 0.1 M, so they had the same concentration, yet 10 drops of iron solution were able to discolor only a few drops of permanganate solution. What can you conclude about the stoichiometry of the reaction?

6. The color change was the result of one of the iron ions being converted to the other oxidation state.
    a. Which of the two equations below best illustrates what happened in the cell for which you observed the color change? Explain how you arrived at your choice.
$$Fe^{2+} \rightarrow Fe^{3+} + e \qquad \text{or} \qquad Fe^{3+} + e \rightarrow Fe^{2+}$$
    b. Is iron being oxidized or reduced? Explain.
    c. Is permanganate ion being oxidized or reduced? Explain.
    d. In the reaction between permanganate and iron ions, which is the oxidizing agent and which is the reducing agent? Explain.
    e. Write the net ionic equation for the reaction. In acidic solution, the manganese atom in the permanganate ion is reduced to manganese(II) ion.

Part D

7. For the reaction between hydrogen peroxide and potassium permanganate:
    a. What difference does the presence of sulfuric acid make? (In the absence of excess acid, the reduction product for permanganate is solid manganese(IV) oxide, rather than manganese(II) ion.)
    b. What must have been the gas you saw bubbling out of the mixture? Defend your choice. (Hint: What happens when hydrogen peroxide spontaneously decomposes?)

    Write the balanced net-ionic equations for the reactions that occurred both with and without addition of sulfuric acid.

8. How does the speed of reaction between permanganate ions and oxalic acid compare with the speed of most of the other reactions in this experiment? What was the effect of warming the system on the speed of reaction?

9. In comparing the reaction of permanganate with hydrogen peroxide and with oxalic acid, was the reaction between potassium permanganate and oxalic acid more like the one with sulfuric acid or the one without? Account for this similarity.

10. In the reaction between $KMnO_4$ and $H_2C_2O_4$, you may have noticed bubbles of gas being produced as the oxalic acid reacted. What gaseous product might have been forming? (Hint: Look at the relative proportions of the elements in the oxalate ion.)

11. The sulfite ion changes vanadium from the 5+ state to the 4+ state.
    a. Is this an oxidation or a reduction?
    b. What must have happened to the sulfite ion in the process? What ion was formed?
    c. Write the net ionic equation for the reaction between the dioxovanadium ion, VO_2^+(aq), and the sulfite ion, SO_3^{2-}(aq). Assume sulfite is oxidized to sulfate ion, and that the reaction takes place in alkaline (basic) solution.

12. a. What effect (oxidation or reduction) does the hypochlorite ion in NaOCl have on vanadium(IV)?
    b. What happens to the vanadium(IV)? (To what is it converted?) How can you tell?
    c. Write the balanced net-ionic equation for the reaction between vanadyl ion, VO^{2+}(aq), and the hypochlorite ion, OCl^-(aq). The other product is chlorine gas, as you could no doubt tell. This process, too, takes place in alkaline solution.

Experiment 6

Analysis by Oxidation-Reduction Titration

Objective

To standardize a potassium permanganate solution, then to use that standardized solution of potassium permanganate to analyze an unknown iron(II) solution

Concepts

Oxidation and reduction, use of primary standards, stoichiometry, quantitative analysis, use of volumetric glassware

Introduction

Probably the most common method used for quantitative analysis of a sample is titration in aqueous solution. Titration involves measured addition of a solution of one of the reactants (the *titrant*), with precisely-know concentration, to a sample of the material to be analyzed (the *analyte*). Traditionally, the titrant is added to the analyte by means of a buret; addition is stopped as soon as the *equivalence point* or *end point* is detected. In strong-acid/strong-base titrations this occurs when the concentrations of hydrogen ions (protons) and hydroxide ions are equal, and is usually detected using an indicator-a compound that is a different color in acid than it is in base.

Oxidation-reduction titrations (*redox titrations*) are more complex. Unlike simple acid-base systems, for which the same type of net process is always involved, each redox system involves a unique net ionic reaction hence a unique stoichiometry. As you know, in any redox reaction the number of electrons lost in oxidation must equal the number of electrons gained in the reduction, but the number of electrons gained and lost not only varies from one species to another, it can even be different when the same substances react under different conditions! Consider the dichromate ion, $Cr_2O_7^{2-}$, with chromium in the 6+ oxidation state. Reduction can convert the chromium to any of three possible lower oxidation states: Cr^{3+}, as in $CrCl_3$; Cr^{2+}, as in $CrSO_4$; or Cr^0, chromium metal. Conversely, metallic chromium may be oxidized by varying the oxidizing agent and/or the reaction medium to a 2+, 3+, or 6+ state. In similar fashion, copper metal reacts with nitric acid to produce copper(II) nitrate. The oxidizing agent is the nitrate ion of the nitric acid, which is reduced from the 5+ state to either the 2+ state (NO) or the 4+ state (NO_2). Which oxide of nitrogen will be produced is determined by the initial concentration of the HNO_3. Permanganate ion, MnO_4^-, reduces to Mn^{2+} in acid, but becomes MnO_2 (the 4+ state) when reduced in an alkaline medium. A primary difficulty in designing a reaction scheme is deciding just what reagents and conditions are necessary to obtain the desired products.

On the positive side, redox titrations often don't require a separate indicator since the color of one or more participants may change as the oxidation state of one of its elements is changed. Some examples: chromium varies from violet to red, orange, and yellow, depending on its oxidation state and the pH of the system; I⁻ is colorless in water and insoluble in organic solvents; while I_2 is yellow in water, due to presence of the triiodide ion, I_3^-, and red or violet in nonpolar solvents. Permanganate ion, containing Manganese(VII), is an inky-dark purple color, but reduction in acidic solution changes it to manganese(II) ion, which is such a faint pink that it appears colorless. It is this change for manganese that will mark the endpoint for your titrations in this experiment.

In any titration, the first task is to determine the strength of the titrant as precisely as possible, since it is the basis for all later calculations. This process is called *standardization*. Careful weighing and proper use of volumetric glassware are not always enough, since the titrant may not be obtainable in high purity, or may react with dissolved gases or other materials in the water. To get a precise value for the concentration of the titrant we use a *primary standard* to *standardize* the titrant before it is used for analysis. The primary standard, a compound of high purity, is generally a solid that can be weighed exactly and used without concern for contamination or side reactions. The primary standard to be used in this experiment is potassium oxalate, $K_2C_2O_4$.

For Part A of this experiment, you will be provided with a solution of potassium oxalate whose concentration is accurately known. You will use that solution to determine the precise concentration of a potassium permanganate solution whose concentration is only approximately known. Because the reaction between permanganate and oxalate ions is slow at room temperature, it will be necessary for you to heat each titration sample.

Then in Part B, the same permanganate solution will be used to analyze an iron(II) compound. The latter reaction proceeds rapidly at room temperature, so heating will not be necessary for Part B.

Prelaboratory Assignment

Read the entire experiment before you begin. Prepare suitable data tables in your notebook for recording the titration data. See the sample in the Processing the Data section of this experiment.

Prelaboratory Questions

1. **a.** The unbalanced equation for the reaction between potassium permanganate and potassium oxalate is:

$$H_2SO_4(aq) + KMnO_4(aq) + K_2C_2O_4(aq) \rightarrow MnSO_4(aq) + CO_2(g) + K_2SO_4(aq) + H_2O(l)$$

Balance the equation using the oxidation number change method. Note that the reaction takes place in the presence of sulfuric acid and that the products include water.

b. Identify the oxidizing agent and the reducing agent in the reaction.

c. What is the mole ratio of potassium permanganate to potassium oxalate in the reaction? What is the mole ratio of sulfuric acid to potassium permanganate in this system? How are these mole ratios reflected in the directions for Part A?

2. Balance the equation for the reaction between solutions of iron(II) sulfate and potassium permanganate.

$$H_2SO_4(aq) + FeSO_4(aq) + KMnO_4(aq) \rightarrow Fe_2(SO_4)_3(aq) + MnSO_4(aq) + H_2O(l)$$

3. The unknown will be a solution of an impure sample of iron(II) sulfate heptahydrate (ferrous sulfate heptahydrate; green vitriol), $FeSO_4 \cdot 7H_2O$. You will determine its purity by comparing the mass percent of iron in a solution containing a known mass of the compound. Determine the theoretical percent by mass of iron in pure $FeSO_4 \cdot 7H_2O$.

4. It is common to assume that dilute aqueous solutions have a density similar to that of pure water, 1.00 g/mL, however the density of the unknown solution prepared for Part B will be significantly greater than 1.00 g/mL; thus, a 25.00-mL solution might have a mass between 25 and 26 grams. Suggest a possible explanation for this.

Safety Precautions

1. Chemical splash-protective eyewear must be worn at all times in the laboratory.

2. Strong acids are highly corrosive to skin and clothing.

3. In addition to being a strong oxidizing agent, potassium permanganate will stain skin and clothing.

Materials

Apparatus

microtip plastic transfer pipettes (4)
milligram balance
labels
10-mL Erlenmeyer flasks
hot plate, steam bath, or hot sand bath

Reagents

$3\ M\ H_2SO_4$
potassium permanganate solution, $KMnO_4(aq)$
standard potassium oxalate solution, $K_2C_2O_4$
phosphoric acid, H_3PO_4
iron(II) salt (unknown)

Procedure

The following abbreviations will be used in this experiment:

PERM	the potassium permanganate solution
OX	the potassium oxalate solution; your primary standard
FE	the iron(II) unknown solution
ACID	3 M sulfuric acid solution

Obtain about 10 mL each of the PERM, OX, and ACID solutions in separate clean, labeled containers. These quantities should be enough to complete the experiment, although you can replace solutions that are consumed, as needed.

Part A: Standardization of Potassium Permanganate by Oxalate Analysis

1. Prepare and label three microtip pipettes as: **ACID** for $3\ M\ H_2SO_4$; **PERM** for the $KMnO_4$ solution that you will standardize; and **OX** for oxalate standard. Fill each from the appropriate stock solution dispenser. Record the identity and concentration given on the dispenser for the oxalate solution. Notice that the concentration is given in units of moles of $K_2C_2O_4$ solution per gram of OX (potassium oxalate solution), thus "mol $K_2C_2O_4$/g OX."

2. Determine the individual masses of the filled **PERM** and **OX** pipettes to the nearest 0.001g; the mass of the sulfuric acid pipette is not needed. Place between 1.0 and 1.5 grams (± 0.001 g) of **OX** (about 1/3 of the capacity of the pipette) in a clean, dry 10-mL flask, and add an approximately-equal volume of $3\ M$ sulfuric acid from your **ACID** pipette. Warm the flask briefly on a hot plate or a steam bath. The solution is hot enough to titrate when the sides of the vessel begin to fog up (about 50 °C).

3. Remove the heated flask from the heat source and begin to add the potassium permanganate solution from your **PERM** pipette, swirling or otherwise agitating the titration vessel constantly, until you have a pink color that persists for at least 30 seconds. If the titration is conducted fairly rapidly, reheating may not be necessary, but it would be a good idea to re-warm the flask briefly every 30–45 seconds to maintain temperature.

   Note: It is important that you keep the contents of the flask well-mixed throughout the titration. If drops of permanganate should collect on the sides of the flask, use a drop or two of 3 $M\ H_2SO_4$ from your **ACID** pipette to rinse them down.

   Record the final masses of the **PERM** and **OX** pipettes after titration is complete.

4. Repeat the titration twice more, for a total of three trials. You should use a fresh flask for each trial, but thoroughly rinse each vessel immediately after use to prevent formation of permanent stains in the glass. If stains do appear, try rinsing with a small amount of 3% hydrogen peroxide antiseptic.

Precision check: Calculate the mass of **PERM** solution used per gram of **OX** for each of the three trials. Determine the mean value for the ratio, then determine the relative deviation. If that relative deviation exceeds 5% of the mean, do one or more additional trials until you have three that show less than 5% deviation.

Part B: Determination of the Purity of a Sample of an Iron(II) Salt
5. Preparation of the Sample Solution

You will be provided with an iron(II) salt whose identity may or may not be given. You are to weigh out a sample having a mass between 0.6 and 0.7 grams ($\pm$ 0.001 g). Quantitatively transfer the sample to a weighed, clean 25-mL volumetric flask. Fill the flask about half-way with distilled water. Swirl the flask to dissolve the sample.

Add about three drops of concentrated phosphoric acid, followed by enough $3M\ H_2SO_4$ to fill about half of the remaining volume. Swirl to mix. If the flask is too full to swirl effectively, cap the flask and invert it several times, with your thumb or finger over the cap to make sure it remains in place.

Finally, use $3M\ H_2SO_4$ to bring the total volume to exactly 25.00 mL of solution. Cap the flask and invert it several times (holding the cap on) to ensure thorough mixing.

Note:　Your teacher may provide you with an acidified solution containing a known mass of an impure iron(II) salt. If so, you will need the mass of salt used and the total mass of solution prepared. These will be on the label of the solution container. If there is a number on the bottle of unknown solution, be sure to record that number. Although the iron solution has been acidified, it cannot hurt to add a couple drops of $3\ M\ H_2SO_4$ to each titration sample, and to use the acid to rinse down any drops of permanganate that get caught on the walls of the flask.

6.　Carry out the titration three separate times, following the procedure given below. As with the standardization in Part A, do additional analyses if necessary to get three that agree within $\pm5\%$ of their mean (average) value. Note that heating the flask is not necessary in this part, nor is addition of an equal volume of 3M sulfuric acid, since the iron solution is already acidified.

7.　Using the unknown iron(II) solution, fill a clean microtip pipette; label it **FE**. Weigh the **FE** pipette and contents, then place about 1.5 gram ($\pm$ 0.001 g) of the iron solution in a clean flask. Refill your **PERM** pipette with the permanganate solution that you standardized in Part A. Weigh the **PERM** pipette and contents, then titrate the iron sample as you did the potassium oxalate, but without heating. As before, you will carry out three trials, weighing both pipettes after each trial, to determine the mass of each solution used in that trial. Clean your flasks after each trial.

Precision check: Calculate the mass of **PERM** solution used per gram of **FE** for each of the three trials. Determine the mean value for the ratio, then determine the relative deviation. If that relative deviation exceeds 5% of the mean, do one or more additional trials until you have three that show less than 5% deviation.

Disposal
Parts A and B
1.　The contents of the titration vessels include manganese, so they cannot be poured down the drain. Transfer them to the container for Transition Metal Waste.

2.　Residual brown stains in the flasks can be removed with 3% hydrogen peroxide (household antiseptic).

3. **Do not return unused reagents—oxalate, permanganate, H₂SO₄, or unknown—to their stock bottles.**

- Reduce leftover permanganate to manganese(II) before transferring it to the container for Transition Metal Waste. The reduction may involve simply combining all of the remaining PERM, OX, ACID, and FE solutions. The final mixture should appear colorless or faintly pink. If it is still purple, add more of the acid and FE solutions.

- Excess potassium oxalate is safe to put down the drain.

- Excess unknown solution must be neutralized before it is poured down the drain.

Processing the Data

Part A: Calculation of Permanganate Concentration

1. Use your data and the balanced equation from prelaboratory question 2 to calculate:
   (i) The number of moles of potassium oxalate used
   (ii) The number of moles of potassium permanganate reacted
   (iii) The concentration of potassium permanganate, in mol KMnO₄/g PERM solution

   Report the individual concentration values for each of your three "best" trials, as well as the mean (average) value and the average deviation (or standard deviation). All calculations for one trial should appear in your notebook, with the results for all trials presented in a summary table.

   Sample summary table headings are shown below. These are samples only; make the ones in your notebook larger, so you have room to write.

	Trial 1	Trial 2	Trial 3
Initial mass of PERM pipette	_____	_____	_____
Final mass of PERM pipette	_____	_____	_____
Mass of PERM	_____	_____	_____
Initial mass of OX pipette	_____	_____	_____
Final mass of OX pipette	_____	_____	_____
Mass of OX	_____	_____	_____
Concentration: _____ mol Na₂C₂O₄/g of oxalate solution	_____	_____	_____
Moles of oxalate delivered	_____	_____	_____
Moles of KMnO₄ present	_____	_____	_____
Concentration of permanganate in mol KMnO₄/g solution	_____	_____	_____

   Average value for permanganate concentration: _____ mol KMnO₄/g solution
   Average permanganate concentration including average deviation: _____

Part B: Calculation of Iron Content

2. Using the equation you balanced in prelaboratory question 3, calculate the number of moles and the mass of iron actually present in each sample and in the entire solution. Calculate the mass of iron in the original unknown solid, from which you (or your teacher) prepared the iron(II) solution. Report the results of your calculations for each individual trial as well as an average value for the percentage of iron. Sample data tables appear below. Calculations for Trial 1 should be in your notebook.

	Trial 1	Trial 2	Trial 3
Initial mass of PERM pipette	_____	_____	_____
Final mass of PERM pipette	_____	_____	_____
Mass of KMnO₄ solution used	_____	_____	_____
Moles of KMnO₄ used	_____	_____	_____
Moles of iron present	_____	_____	_____
Initial mass of FE pipette	_____	_____	_____
Final mass of FE pipette	_____	_____	_____
Mass of iron solution used	_____	_____	_____
Concentration of iron (in mol Fe²⁺/g solution)	_____	_____	_____

Mass of 25.00-mL solution

Moles of iron in 25.00 mL solution

Mass of iron in 25.00 mL solution

Mass of solid used to make solution

% iron in unknown solid

Average value for % iron: _____

Average percentage of iron, including average deviation: _____

Analysis and Conclusions

1. Suppose your solid contained some iron(III) as a result of air-oxidation of iron(II). How would this affect your results? Would your values for the percentage of iron come out too high or too low? Be as specific as you can.

2. In the absence of excess hydrogen ion, reduction of permanganate solution yields a brown, insoluble material, MnO_2. If permanganate solution is allowed to cling to the walls of the test tube, brown stains develop as a result of MnO_2 formation. How is the mole ratio of MnO_4^- to Fe^{2+} affected by this change? (Hint: Consider the oxidation states of manganese in MnO_4^-, MnO_2, and Mn^{2+}.) What effect would this change of products have on your determinations? Explain.

3. In fact, a small amount of conversion of manganese(II) to manganese(IV) oxide is almost unavoidable. If such occurrences result in a mass of permanganate solution used that is off by 5 mg, what would be the percentage error in your value for the concentration of the permanganate titrant, determined in Part A? Is this a systematic or random error? Explain.

4. To determine the purity of the iron salt you analyzed, divide the experimental value for the mass percent of iron (from Processing the Data #2) by the theoretical mass percent of iron in the salt, based on the formula of the solid. (If your unknown was iron(II) sulfate heptahydrate, you calculated this value in Prelaboratory Question #4). Report this value of the percent purity along with the experimental and theoretical percentages of iron.

Experiment 7

Molar Mass by Vapor Density:
The Dumas Method

Objective

To determine the approximate molar mass of a volatile liquid by vapor density measurement

Concepts

Gas laws, Avogadro's hypothesis

Introduction

The determination of the molecular weight of a molecule is of fundamental importance in chemistry. Combustion analysis may indicate that a molecule has the empirical formula CH_2; if the molar mass is found to be 84 g/mol, the compound must have a molecular formula of C_6H_{12}. Molar mass can be determined in more than a dozen different ways. This experiment explores one of them: the *vapor density method*.

A liquid that vaporizes easily under normal conditions is said to be *volatile*. Use of the vapor density of a volatile liquid to determine molar mass is a method originated by Jean-Baptiste Dumas in the early 1800s. One consequence of Avogadro's Hypothesis is that the number of moles of gas in a sample is directly related to the pressure, volume, and absolute temperature of the system. The procedure used in this experiment is a simplified version of more sophisticated methods used in research. At best, the method involves a fairly high degree of uncertainty: $\geq 10\%$ error must be anticipated. Even so, it is adequate for those situations in which greater precision is not required. Consider, for example, a case in which one is trying to decide whether a particular chlorinated hydrocarbon is monochloromethane or dichloromethane: CH_3Cl or CH_2Cl_2; because the molar mass of dichloromethane is about 85, while that of the monochloro- compound is only about 51, it is a simple matter to distinguish between them. On the other hand, the molar masses of cyclohexane (C_6H_{12}, MW = 84) and cyclohexene (C_6H_{10}, MW = 82) are far closer together than the $\pm 10\%$ uncertainty.

If this experiment were to be carried out very carefully we would want to know the exact temperature of the vapor in the flask. This could be done by immersing the flask in a large beaker of water at a known temperature, e.g. 100°C (boiling water). We would want to know the atmospheric pressure at the time of each run. Instead we are *assuming* in this experiment that the temperature of the gas is 4.0 x 10^2 K and that the atmospheric pressure is 1.0 atm. As part of your analysis, you will calculate how far from these assumptions of 4.0 x 10^2 K, and 1.0 atm you would need to be in order to exceed the goal of $\pm 10\%$ accuracy in the molar mass.

You will fill a container of known volume with the vapor of the compound whose molecular weight is to be determined, at a known temperature and pressure. The flask is weighed empty, the liquid is added, then the flask is heated, vaporizing the sample and allowing it to more than fill the container. Air is flushed out of the flask in the process and excess vapor of the unknown escapes through a pinhole opening in the covering of the flask. After cooling, the flask is weighed again, this time with the condensed sample whose vapors just filled the flask at atmospheric pressure. The Ideal Gas Law is used to calculate the number of moles of material present in the flask; from the mass of the sample and the number of moles present, the molar mass, in grams per mole, is readily determined.

Note: The term *molar mass* is a relatively new one. Originally, chemists referred to atomic weights and molecular weights, ignoring the distinction between mass and weight (which is minor at best, near sea level). The symbol for molecular weight is MW. Since there is no agreed-upon symbol for molar mass, we will use MW in this experiment.

Prelaboratory Assignment

1. Read the entire experiment before you begin.

2. Prepare a data table in your notebook for recording the data to be collected. Note that you will be conducting three trials, but the only piece of information that won't be the same for all three is the mass of the flask with the condensed vapor.

Prelaboratory Questions

1. Solve the Ideal Gas Law for the number of moles of gas, **n**.

2. Write an expression for the molecular weight, **MW**, in terms of the sample mass, **m**, and the number of moles, **n**.

3. Write an expression for the molecular weight, **MW**, in terms of **P**, **V**, **T** and the sample mass, **m**.

Safety Precautions

1. Chemical splash-protective eyewear must be worn at all times in the laboratory.

2. Contact lenses should not be worn when organic vapors are present; this is especially true of plastic lenses, which absorb or dissolve in the vapors. If contacts are your only option, take extra precaution in keeping the liquids and vapors away from your eyes. Remove your goggles only when you are completely outside the laboratory.

3. Organic liquids are flammable; there must be no open flames in the same room while you are working with them.

4. Avoid breathing the vapors of organic liquids; work only in a well-ventilated space.

5. The organic liquids are toxic by ingestion. Wash your hands thoroughly with soap and water before leaving the laboratory.

Materials

Apparatus

milligram balance
100-mL round bottom flask
flask heater (100 mL Thermowell) and controller
aluminum foil
copper wire
250-mL graduated cylinder
safety goggles

Reagents

unknown volatile liquid

Procedure

The following steps are to be carried out three times in all. Between trials, it is not necessary to clean the flask. Simply add a bit more of the liquid you are using.

1. Set the controller of the flask heater (100 mL Thermowell or similar) to 15% power; this will heat the walls of the heater to 400 K (Fig. 35.1). Weigh together on the balance a 100-mL round-bottom flask, a piece of aluminum foil about 5 cm square and a piece of small-diameter copper

wire about 15 cm long. Be sure the foil does not touch anything other than the balance pan. Add about 1 or 2 milliliters of the unknown to the flask, then carefully fold the foil over the top of the flask, securing it to the flask with the piece of wire. Poke a small pin-hole in the center of the foil.

2. Place the flask in the well of the flask heater; the sample will boil, forcing the air from the flask, then fill the space with its own vapor. At this point, no liquid should be visible in the flask. If the liquid has a relatively high boiling point, total vaporization may be difficult to achieve and the liquid may begin to *reflux*, as indicated by rivulets of liquid running down the inside of the flask. If this happens, wrap a cone of foil (about 20 cm square, larger if necessary) around the top of the flask, allowing it to extend down far enough that it surrounds the top of the heater. This traps the heat and better warms the neck of the flask; vaporization should be complete in 5–10 minutes.

3. Remove the flask from the heater, allow it to cool to room temperature, then weigh the covered flask containing the now-condensed sample. (Do not include the foil "tent," if one was used in the preceding step.) Again, be certain that the foil does not touch the sides of the balance.

   Carefully remove the foil cap and add about 1 mL of the unknown. Re-cover the flask with the same foil piece and carry out a second trial. Calculate the mass of condensed vapor for each of your two trials and compare the results to see if additional runs are necessary to achieve ±10% agreement. If the mass of condensed vapor differs by less than 10.%, you need not do a third trial. Otherwise, repeat step 3 until you have three values that agree within 10.% of their mean value.

4. When all trials have been completed, carry out the cleanup as directed below in Disposal, then proceed with the determination of the volume of the flask. (A 100-mL flask will contain more than 100-mL of vapor; the neck of the flask is not figured into the nominal size.)

Disposal

Your instructor will tell you which waste receptacle to use for any liquid remaining in your flask and will indicate what special cleaning methods may be necessary. Once cleaning is complete and the flask is dry, carry out step 5, the volume determination.

Volume Determination

5. Once your final trial has been completed, waste material has been disposed of and the flask is clean, you can measure the actual volume of the flask. To do this, fill the flask with water to the top rim of the neck, simulating the flask filled with vapor. Carefully transfer the water from the flask to a 250-mL graduated cylinder; read and record the volume to the nearest milliliter. The flask now may be emptied, dried, and put away.

Sample Data Table	Trial 1	Trial 2	Trial 3
Mass of flask plus sample	_____	_____	_____
Mass of flask (Note 1)	_____	_____	_____
Mass of sample	_____	_____	_____
Volume of flask (Note 2)	_____		

Notes:
1. The "mass of flask" includes the foil and wire. It is determined only once, before the first trial.
2. The volume of the flask is to be determined only once, in step 5, following the final trial.

Processing the Data (All calculations are to be shown in the notebook.)

1. For each trial, calculate the number of moles of vapor in the flask, using your measured volume and the ideal gas law. Assume a temperature of 4.0×10^2 K and a pressure of 1.0 atm, unless otherwise directed.

2. The molar mass (molecular weight) of the unknown is found using the equation you derived for prelaboratory question **5**. Report the individual values for molar mass, as well as an average (mean) value. Calculate and report the percent deviation, as well.

3. If your instructor gives you a list of possible unknowns, select the one that most closely matches your results. If the empirical formula for your sample is given, determine the molecular formula.

    If neither piece of information is supplied, simply determine the formula for a hydrocarbon that would have the molar mass you determined. Assume that the hydrocarbon has an empirical formula of either C_nH_{2n+2} (alkanes) or C_nH_{2n} (alkenes and cycloalkanes).

Analysis and Conclusions

Question numbers 3–6 call for in-depth analysis; single-sentence responses will likely be inadequate.

1. Assuming all measurements except temperature were made correctly, how large an error in temperature would be needed to give an error of *more than* 10% in the molar mass?

2. Now assuming all measurements except for *pressure* were made correctly, how far off would the pressure measurement have to be to result in an error of more than 10% in the molar mass?

3. Based on your answers to questions 1 and 2, discuss the validity of assuming a value of 400K for the flask heater temperature and 1.0 atm for the atmospheric pressure in the first experiment. Discuss the likelihood of either errors occurring with the magnitudes you determined above.

4. Why is the mass of air in the flask neglected during the calculations?

5. The vapor is treated as an ideal gas during the calculations. In what way(s) does this represent an unrealistic assumption? Discuss fully. (Hint: Under what types of conditions would assumption of ideal gas behavior be least likely to be valid?)

6. If the time of heating is insufficient to allow complete evaporation of the sample, what will be the effect on your value for molecular weight? (Answers such as "It will be incorrect" will receive no credit. Will it be too high or too low? Why?)

7. What physical property or properties of the liquids used for this experiment governed your teacher's choice of suitable unknowns for this experiment?

Experiment 8

Heats of Reaction and Hess's Law

Objective

To verify Hess's Law of Additivity of Reaction Enthalpies

Concepts

Enthalpy, Calorimetry, Hess's Law

Introduction

Reactions generally involve the transfer of energy either into or out of the reaction system. When heat is released during the course of a reaction we say the reaction is *exothermic*; when the system absorbs energy, the reaction is *endothermic*. The energy represents the difference in bond energies between the product molecules and the reactant molecules. As a simple example, consider the combustion of methane, CH_4. The reaction is shown first as molecular formulas, then using structural formulas to show the bonds between atoms.

$$CH_4(g) + 2\ O_2(g) \rightarrow CO_2(g) + 2\ H_2O(g)$$

In order for the reaction to occur, the four C–H bonds in methane must be broken, as must the two double bonds joining the pairs of oxygen atoms; this requires an input of energy at least equal to the potential energy represented by those bonds. When the new bonds form, energy is released. As you might expect, each type of bond ($C=O$, $C-H$, $H-O$, and $O=O$) involves a unique quantity of energy, thus the energy released during bond formation will generally be different from the quantity absorbed in breaking the bonds of the reactants. Since the amount of energy depends directly on the number of molecules involved in the reaction, reaction energies are generally expressed in units of kilojoules per mole (kJ/mol) of some reactant or product. This quantity of energy is represented by ΔH, and the sign of ΔH reveals whether the reaction is endothermic (ΔH is positive) or exothermic (ΔH is negative). For our example reaction, the accepted value of the heat of reaction is -890 kJ/mol, meaning that 890 kJ of energy are released for each mole (16 g) of methane burned. In other words, there were 890 kJ more energy in the bonds of one CH_4 and two O_2 molecules than are stored in the bonds of the one CO_2 and two H_2O molecules.

Here's an important point: If the reaction between methane, CH_4, and oxygen gas, O_2, releases 890 kJ in producing CO_2 and H_2O, then the reverse reaction:

$$CO_2(g) + 2\ H_2O(g) \rightarrow CH_4(g) + 2\ O_2(g)$$

must absorb exactly 890 kJ. Why? Because all the bonds that were broken when methane burned are now being formed. And the bonds that were formed in the production of CO_2 and H_2O are now being broken. In other words, if you reverse the direction of a reaction, you must change the sign of the energy change that accompanies that reaction.

In 1840, G.H. Hess recognized that the energy change that accompanies a reaction depends only on what the reactants and products are, not on the way in which one is converted to the other. This came to be known as Hess's Law. It will be your goal in this experiment to demonstrate for yourself that this statement is a valid one. To do that, you will measure the energy change for two different reactions, then combine them to predict the energy change for another reaction. Here are the three reactions; notice that all species that ionize in water are shown as ions, while solids and non-ionizing substances are shown in molecular form.

(1) The dissolving of sodium hydroxide in water:

$$NaOH(s) \quad \rightarrow \quad Na^+(aq) + OH^-(aq) \qquad (8\text{-}1)$$

(2) The reaction between solid sodium hydroxide and acetic acid:

$$NaOH(s) + HC_2H_3O_2(aq) \quad \rightarrow \quad H_2O(l) + Na^+(aq) + C_2H_3O_2^-(aq) \qquad (8\text{-}2)$$

(3) The reaction between aqueous solutions of sodium hydroxide and acetic acid:

$$Na^+(aq) + OH^-(aq) + HC_2H_3O_2(aq) \quad \rightarrow \quad H_2O(l) + Na^+(aq) + C_2H_3O_2^-(aq) \qquad (8\text{-}3)$$

As noted above, you will measure the heats of reactions for the first two, then combine them to predict the quantity of heat that will be transferred in the third reaction. You will then measure the heat transfer of the third reaction directly to see how close your prediction came. The method of combining the first two reactions is the subject of the Prelaboratory Questions. The apparatus may be familiar to you from other experiments.

Procedure Note: This experiment can be done with a digital thermometer or with a temperature probe interfaced to a computer or to a hand-held device. Your teacher will advise you of the setup to be used.

Prelaboratory Assignment

1. Read the entire experiment before coming to the laboratory.

2. Prepare a Data Table for Part 1 with the following headings:

Reaction Equation	Mass of Solid NaOH used	Initial Temp. (°C)	Final Temp. (°C)	ΔT (°C)

Prelaboratory Questions

1. Rewrite equation *(8-3)* of the introduction in net ionic form.

2. Recopy equations *(8-1)* and *(8-2)* from the introduction, but reverse equation *(8-1)* so that solid sodium hydroxide appears on the products side of the arrow and the dissolved ions appear as reactants. Now add the two equations, just as you would in algebra when solving two equations in two unknowns, to show that the result you obtained by combining equations *(8-1)* and *(8-2)* is identical to the net ionic equation version of equation *(8-3)*.

3. All three reactions that you will carry out in this experiment will result in temperature increases. Are the reactions endothermic or exothermic? Explain.

4. You will use approximately 2.00 g of solid sodium hydroxide in two of the three reactions. Convert 2.00 g of NaOH to moles of NaOH.

Safety Precautions

1. Chemical splash-protective eyewear must be worn at all times in the laboratory.

2. Sodium hydroxide is extremely caustic; avoid contact with skin and clothing. If it gets on your skin, rinse the affected area with water until it no longer feels slippery. Use large amounts of water to clean up spills on surfaces.

3. While acetic acid is considered a weak acid, it should be considered corrosive. Handle skin contact and spills as you would any acid spill.

4. Wash your hands thoroughly with soap and water before leaving the laboratory.

Materials

Apparatus

digital thermometer or
   interfaced temperature probe
foamed polystyrene cups (3)
beaker, 250-mL, to hold calorimeter
weighing boat or small beaker, as a
   weighing container for solid NaOH
graduated cylinder, 50- or 100-mL
graduated cylinders, 25-mL (2)

Reagents

sodium hydroxide pellets, $NaOH(s)$
sodium hydroxide, $NaOH(aq)$, 2.0 M
acetic acid, $HC_2H_3O_2(aq)$, 1.0 M
acetic acid, $HC_2H_3O_2(aq)$, 2.0 M

Procedure

Note: You will have to work quickly and efficiently while carrying out the first two reactions, each involving solid sodium hydroxide. The NaOH pellets will absorb water rapidly from the air. This will make them tend to stick to the weighing container.

1. Assemble the calorimeter as shown at the right. Two cups are placed in the beaker for stability, then the third cup is trimmed about 1 cm below the rim. This permits it to be inverted and used as a lid. It should fit snugly into the opening of the other two cups.

   Make a small hole in the lid, just large enough to accept the thermometer or probe. Most digital thermometers have pointed tips, so they can make their own opening. The tighter the fit, the better the calorimeter will contain the heat that is released by the reactions.

   Once the temperature probe has been inserted into the calorimeter lid, avoid moving it any more than necessary, to maintain the snug fit.

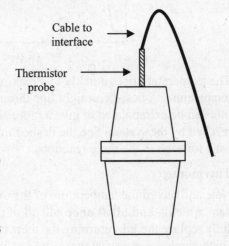

Cable to interface

Thermistor probe

**Calorimeter Apparatus, with
Interfaced Temperature Probe.**
(The 250-mL beaker is used only
for support, so it is not shown
here.)

2. If you are using an interfaced temperature probe, set up the software to take readings every second for a period of 240 seconds. If you are asked for a temperature range, select 0°C to 50°C.

Do not start collecting data yet.

If you are using a digital thermometer, you will have to monitor the temperature on your own. Record the initial temperature of the liquid in the calorimeter, then watch it steadily, noting the highest temperature reached. A run of four minutes should be enough for the temperature to reach a maximum, and perhaps even start back down. See **step 5b**.

3. Use the large graduate to place 50.0 mL of distilled water into the calorimeter. Place the lid containing the thermometer or temperature probe on the calorimeter.

4. Into your small beaker or weighing boat, weigh 2.00 g of NaOH pellets.

Note: The pellets are of varying size, and you may not be able to get 2.00 grams exactly. Get as close as you can and record the actual mass of NaOH used, ± 0.01 g. Do not spend time trying to get 2.00 grams exactly.

5. a. **Interfaced Temperature Probe**

Allow the unit to record the acetic acid temperature a few times, then remove the lid as you **quickly and all at once** add all of the sodium hydroxide pellets. Carefully replace the lid, returning the probe to the solution. Hold the apparatus in both hands and gently swirl the calorimeter. This is necessary to ensure that the pellets dissolve entirely. If some solid remains when you open the calorimeter you will have to repeat that trial.

At the conclusion of the run examine your data, looking for the initial temperature of the water and the highest temperature reached. If your interface can plot the data, it will probably give you a plot with the following shape:

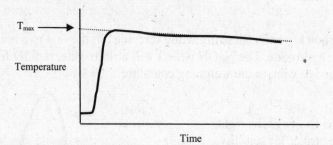

The temperature rises quickly to a maximum, levels briefly, then starts to return toward room temperature. A best-fit straight line through the portion that starts with the maximum on the plot can be extrapolated to give a more accurate value for the actual maximum temperature reached by the system. See the dashed line in the sketch. This extrapolation technique can be used for each of the three reactions.

b. **Thermometer**

Note and record the temperature of the distilled water in the calorimeter. Once temperature is constant, **quickly and all at once** add all of the sodium hydroxide pellets. Quickly and carefully replace the lid, returning the thermometer to the solution. Holding the apparatus with both hands, gently swirl the entire assembly to help the pellets dissolve in the acid. If some solid remains when you open the calorimeter you will have to repeat that trial.

6. Lift the calorimeter lid and use a wash bottle to rinse the thermometer or probe, collecting the rinsings in the calorimeter cup. The solution is essentially 1 M NaOH, so it must be neutralized. See **Disposal: Reaction (1)** for instructions.

7. **Reaction 2:** Rinse the inside of the calorimeter with distilled water, blot it dry lightly and gently with paper towel, then repeat the experiment using 50.0 mL of 1.0 M acetic acid, $HC_2H_3O_2(aq)$,

in place of the distilled water. Again, weigh out the sodium hydroxide quickly, getting as close as you can to 2.00 g, but do not waste time trying to get that mass precisely. Record the actual mass used.

Follow the appropriate procedure of step 5 to determine the quantity of heat released when solid sodium hydroxide dissolves in, and reacts with, 1.0 M acetic acid. At the conclusion of the run, lift the calorimeter lid and use a wash bottle to rinse the probe or thermometer, catching the rinsings in the calorimeter cup, then follow the clean-up instructions in **Disposal, Reactions (2) and (3)**.

8. Repeat the experiment, using 25.0 mL each of 2.0 M sodium hydroxide solution and 2.0 M acetic acid. The 2.0 M $HC_2H_3O_2$ acid is placed in the clean, dried calorimeter. The experiment begins when the 2.0 M NaOH is added quickly and quantitatively. This time you can expect the temperature to rise more sharply, then begin to fall after about 2 minutes.

Disposal

1. **Reaction (1):** To the contents of the calorimeter, add 50. mL of 1.0 M acetic acid to neutralize the sodium hydroxide. The contents can now be flushed down the drain with large amounts of water.

2. **Reactions (2) and (3):** Rinse the temperature probe with distilled water, catching the rinsings in the calorimeter. The solution remaining in the calorimeter is essentially neutral and may be rinsed down the drain with water.

3. If you used an interfaced temperature probe, your teacher will direct you regarding what to do with the probe and interface. Be sure the thermometer or temperature probe has been cleaned and dried before putting it away.

4. The calorimeter lids may be discarded in the waste basket unless your teacher directs you to leave them for another use. The two calorimeter cups are to be rinsed thoroughly and blotted dry. They can be saved for another use.

Processing the Data

1. Use the equation $q = s \times m \times \Delta T$ to calculate the quantity of heat, q, released in each of the three processes. In each case, assume that the solution in the calorimeter has the same specific heat capacity as water, 4.18 J/g °C. Assume that the acetic acid and NaOH solutions have densities of 1.0 g/mL. Remember to include the mass of solid sodium hydroxide when determining m for reactions (1) and (2).

2. In the first two reactions, you used solid sodium hydroxide. Convert the actual masses of sodium hydroxide used to moles. Show your work.

3. The quantities and concentrations of the two solutions used in Reaction 3 were chosen so that 0.0500 moles of sodium hydroxide would be present. Use this information and the numbers of moles of NaOH you calculated in question 2 to convert your values of q from question 1 to ΔH values, in kJ/mol NaOH.

Analysis and Conclusions

1. Recall that when you combined equations *(8-1)* and *(8-2)* in prelaboratory question 2, you reversed the direction of Reaction *(8-1)*. This changes the sign, but not the magnitude, of ΔH for that reaction. Refer to question 3 of Processing the Data to determine values for ΔH_1, ΔH_2, and ΔH_3 as identified below. Watch signs and be sure to include appropriate units.

$$Na^+(aq) + OH^-(aq) \rightarrow NaOH(s) \qquad\qquad\qquad \Delta H_1$$

$$NaOH(s) + HC_2H_3O_2(aq) \rightarrow H_2O(l) + Na^+(aq) + C_2H_3O_2^-(aq) \qquad \Delta H_2$$

$$Na^+(aq) + OH^-(aq) + HC_2H_3O_2(aq) \rightarrow H_2O(l) + Na^+(aq) + C_2H_3O_2^-(aq) \qquad \Delta H_3$$

2. Calculate the sum of ΔH_1 and ΔH_2. Show your work.

3. Because the sum of the first two equations of question 1 is the same as the third equation, the combined values of ΔH_1 and ΔH_2 should equal the value of ΔH_3. Determine the percent deviation between the sum of $(\Delta H_1 + \Delta H_2)$ and the value you obtained experimentally for ΔH_3 by dividing the difference by the value for ΔH_3. Note the absolute value signs in the equation.

$$\frac{|\{\Delta H_1 + \Delta H_2\} - \{\Delta H_3\}|}{\Delta H_3} \text{ x } 100\% = \% \text{ deviation}$$

4. In Processing the Data #1, you were told to assume that all three solutions had about the same specific heat capacity as water. Explain why that assumption is reasonably valid for reactions (2) and (3), but less so for reaction (1).

5. In terms of the actual processes that are occurring in the three reactions, explain why the enthalpy change for the second reaction should equal the sum of the enthalpy changes for the first and third reactions. (**Note:** This is not the same combination for which you calculated a net ΔH in questions 1 and 2, above.)

6. In this, as in all the calorimetry experiments you may have done, some loss of heat to the surroundings is unavoidable. Of the three processes you carried out in this experiment, which one is likely to have the greatest such transfer of heat? Defend your choice.

7. Suggest a reason for drying the inner cup of the calorimeter between trials.

Experiment 9

Analysis by Calorimetry

Objective

To use calorimetry to determine the stoichiometry of a reaction

Concepts

Calorimetry, heats of reaction, stoichiometry

Introduction

In this experiment, you will explore how the enthalpy change for a reaction can be used to deduce the products of a reaction system. The system under investigation here is the reaction between sodium thiosulfate and dilute household bleach, an aqueous solution of sodium hypochlorite. The hypochlorite ion, OCl^-, is an oxidizing agent. The sulfur atoms in thiosulfate, $S_2O_3^{2-}$, have an oxidation state of 2+. Thiosulfate can be oxidized to either sulfite, SO_3^{2-}, or to sulfate, SO_4^{2-}. Your objective is to determine which of these is actually produced.

The first step in your analysis will be to determine the enthalpy changes that result when the reactant solutions are mixed in varying proportions. From the value of q for each combination, and from knowledge of the number of moles of each reactant present, you will be able to calculate an observed value of ΔH, in kJ/mol, for each trial. The combination that gives the greatest value of ΔH will be the one that has the correct reaction stoichiometry. Because the stoichiometry depends on the oxidation state of sulfur in the products, you can use this stoichiometric ratio to determine whether sulfite or sulfate results from the oxidation of thiosulfate.

You will mix the reactants in a series of volume ratios and measure the temperature change in each case. For each trial you will use a total of 30.0 mL of the combined solutions. Since both reactant solutions are 0.50 M, the volume ratio will be the same as the mole ratio for that combination of reactants. Thus, a trial in which 10.0 mL of sodium thiosulfate is added to 20.0 mL of dilute bleach would have a 1:2 mole ratio of thiosulfate ion to hypochlorite ion.

The Procedure assumes that you will use an interfaced thermistor probe. If instead you use a digital thermometer, you will need to manually record the initial temperature of the first reactant solution and the maximum temperature reached by each solution combination.

Prelaboratory Assignment

1. Read the entire experiment before you begin.

2. Prepare a data table for recording the temperature changes for each trial. The first three columns of your table should duplicate the table of mixing ratios, Table 9-1, found on page 43. There should be three additional columns: one for the mole ratios that you will calculate in Prelaboratory Question 3a, one for the initial temperature for each trial, and one for the highest temperature reached in that trial.

Prelaboratory Questions

1. Hypochlorite is an oxidizing agent. In this system the thiosulfate ion is oxidized to either sulfite or sulfate ions. The chlorine atom in the OCl^- ion will be reduced to chloride ion.
   a. Write the balanced net ionic equation for the reaction between thiosulfate and hypochlorite to produce sulfite ion and chloride ion. Remember this is an alkaline system so hydroxide ions (from sodium hydroxide) and water will also be involved.

  b. Now write the balanced net ionic equation for the same system assuming the products to be
      chloride and the sulfate ion, rather than sulfite.

  c. How will you decide which of the two equations correctly represents the reaction between
      sulfite and hypochlorite?

2. a. Determine the mole ratio of hypochlorite to thiosulfate for each of the nine combinations that
        you will test. (Recall that they are the same as the volume ratios.)

  b. Which trial will give the greatest value of ΔH if sulfite is one of the products? Which trial
      will identify sulfate as the product?

Safety Precautions

1. Chemical splash-protective eyewear must be worn at all times in the laboratory.

2. Sodium hypochlorite (bleach) is a skin irritant. Avoid contact with skin. The sodium thiosulfate
    solution is strongly alkaline. Avoid skin contact and wipe up any spills immediately. Wash your
    hands thoroughly with soap and water before leaving the laboratory.

Materials

Apparatus   *Reagents*

50-mL beaker   sodium hypochlorite, NaOCl, 0.50 M
100-mL beaker   sodium thiosulfate, $Na_2S_2O_3$, 0.50 M,
250-mL beakers (2, to hold reagent solutions)   in 1.1 M NaOH
paper towels   distilled water (wash bottle)
foam polystyrene cup, 6-oz (1)   **(Optional)**
25-mL graduated cylinders (2)   sodium sulfite, Na_2SO_3, 0.50 M
thermometer or interfaced temperature probe   sodium iodide, NaI, 0.50 M

Procedure

Note 1:   Always place the reactant solution for which the volume is larger in the calorimeter first.
          Although varying the order of mixing may introduce another variable, it is done to ensure
          that the thermometer or temperature probe is sufficiently submerged.

Note 2:   The reaction in each case will be pretty rapid. If you are using an interfaced probe, set the
          time interval to 1 second, with a run time of 2 minutes.

1. Prepare the calorimeter setup as illustrated in Figure 9-1, on the next page. The system consists of
    a 50-mL beaker, wrapped in a paper towel for insulation, then inserted into a 100-mL beaker. The
    lid is an inverted 6-oz expanded polystyrene cup; the probe or thermometer is inserted through
    the lid as shown in Figure 9-2.

2. Label separate 25-mL graduated cylinders for the two reactant solutions, $Na_2S_2O_3$ and NaOCl.
    Keep these two separate to avoid contamination.

3. Each trial follows the same basic sequence:

  a. The desired volume of the reagent that is to be in excess is placed into the inner beaker of the
      calorimeter and allowed to stand briefly to establish thermal equilibrium.

  b. The lid containing the temperature probe is placed on the calorimeter and the run is started,
      with the interface recording the temperature of the solution.

c. The lid is removed and the second reagent is added *all at once*. The lid, containing the probe, is immediately returned to cover the calorimeter and the calorimeter system is gently swirled to ensure complete mixing.

d. The highest temperature reached by the system is noted and recorded, as was the temperature of the system with only the first reagent.

e. The lid is removed and the contents of the system are rinsed down the drain.

f. The inner beaker of the calorimeter is rinsed with distilled water *and dried*, in preparation for the next trial.

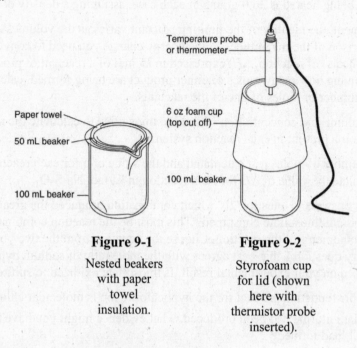

Figure 9-1	Figure 9-2
Nested beakers with paper towel insulation.	Styrofoam cup for lid (shown here with thermistor probe inserted).

Table 9-1: Mixing Ratios

Trial	Sodium Hypochlorite	Sodium Thiosulfate
1	25.0 mL	5.0 mL
2	24.0	6.0
3	22.5	7.5
4	20.0	10.0
5	15.0	15.0
6	10.0	20.0
7	7.5	22.5
8	6.0	24.0
9	5.0	25.0

Disposal

1. All solutions remaining after the reaction is complete may safely be poured down the drain, as may unused bleach and sodium thiosulfate solution. Before washing them down, mix all reagents together and allow the mixture to cool, then pour it down the drain with the water running.

2. Clean all glassware and return it to its proper location.

3. Your teacher will instruct you about what to do with the foam cups and temperature measuring apparatus.

4. Wash your hands thoroughly before leaving the laboratory.

Analysis and Conclusions

1. You carried out nine reactions. For each one, determine the temperature change, ΔT, then calculate q^1, the quantity of heat released during the reaction. Assume that each of the solution combinations has the same specific heat capacity as water, 4.18 J/g °C. Note also that the total mass of water being heated is 30.0 grams in each case, assuming a density of 1.0 g/mL.

2. In this experiment, the identity of the limiting reactant varies as the volumes are changed. To get a valid comparison of the magnitudes of the energy change you need to convert your values of q to enthalpies (heats) of reaction, ΔH, expressed in kJ/mol of a reactant or product. Since you have no way of knowing how many moles of either product are being formed, calculation must be based on the number of moles of one of the reactants.

   a. Use the volume and concentration of sodium thiosulfate to calculate the number of moles of thiosulfate ion present in each reaction system.

   b. Use the number of moles just calculated and the value of q for each reaction (from question 1) to calculate the value of ΔH for each reaction in kJ/mol $Na_2S_2O_3$.

3. Based on your answers to question 2b, which combination produced the greatest amount of heat per mole of sodium thiosulfate consumed? This must be the reaction combination that represents the actual stoichiometry of the reaction. Choose the equation from the two you wrote in response to prelaboratory question 2 that best agrees with the mole ratio of sodium hypochlorite to sodium thiosulfate based on your experimental result. Is thiosulfate oxidized to sulfite or to sulfate?

4. Another possible reduction product for the hypochlorite ion is molecular chlorine, Cl_2.

   a. If molecular chlorine had been produced, what evidence might you have had that would tell you that Cl_2 had formed?

   b. Write the balanced net ionic equation for formation of molecular chlorine and the sulfur-containing ion that you chose for question 3. Would formation of Cl_2 instead of Cl^- have had any effect on your ability to distinguish between sulfite and sulfate as possible reaction products? Explain.

5. Recall that the sodium thiosulfate solution was prepared using 1.1 M NaOH as the solvent, rather than distilled water. Does that fact alone suggest which of the two product ions, sulfite or sulfate, is produced? Explain.

Further Investigation

1. You were told to base your decision on the number of moles of sodium sulfite consumed. That was an arbitrary choice. Do the calculations necessary to show that the same results would be obtained and the same decision would have been made had you based your calculations in question 2b on the moles of sodium hypochlorite consumed, instead of on moles of sodium thiosulfate.

2. Repeat the experiment using the same concentrations and volume combinations, but replace the sodium thiosulfate with either sodium sulfite, Na_2SO_3, or sodium iodide. Follow the instructions for the original experiment.

---

[1] $q = s \; x \; m \; x \; \Delta T$; where s is the specific heat capacity of the system.

Experiment 10

Chemistry of the Halogens

Objectives

To distinguish chemically among the halide ions and to establish an activity series for members of the halogen family

Concepts

Solubility and precipitation, qualitative analysis, activity series

Introduction

Group 7A, called the halogens, consists of fluorine, chlorine, bromine, and iodine. (All isotopes of astatine are radioactive, so astatine generally is omitted from experiments such as this.) This experiment is in two parts, which you may do in a single laboratory session or spread over two periods. In the first part, you will learn how to distinguish the halide ions from one another and how to determine which (if any) of the ions may be present in an unknown. Such a process is called *qualitative analysis*. In the second part, you will experimentally establish the relative order of reactivity, or *activity series*, for the halogens. Because the two parts are very different from each other, they will be introduced separately.

Part A: Qualitative Analysis of the Halide Group

The term *halide ion* refers to any of the ions, F^-, Cl^-, Br^-, or I^-. You will be given solutions of known halide ion content, along with several other solutions (*test reagents*) to use in order to see how each reacts with a particular halide ion in solution. By carefully keeping track of how each halide ion reacts, especially in terms of solubility, you will be able to identify them as unknowns, even if two halide ions are present in the same solution.

Part B: Halogen Activity Series

Elements are described as being *active* if they tend to react with other elements to form compounds readily; in that sense, the word active really means "reactive." In contrast to metals, which can only form ionic bonds, nonmetals can form compounds either by ionic bonding or by covalent bonding. When they bond ionically, nonmetals tend to gain electrons, forming anions. Covalent bonding results from the sharing of electrons, as one atom donates electrons to another to fill available orbitals in each. Thus, an active nonmetal is one that has a strong tendency to acquire electrons. In other words, the free (uncombined) element is readily reduced to its ion form, but the ion form is not easily oxidized to the free element.

Just as oil and water don't mix in salad dressings, so many organic liquids are not able to mix with water. These liquids are referred to as being nonpolar. You probably learned about polar and nonpolar molecules in your first chemistry course. The nonpolar liquid you will use is either hexane, C_6H_{12}, a pure substance, or a mixture known as petroleum ether or ligroin, which contains alkanes of five, six, and seven carbon atoms.

As you might recall, substances such as table salt that dissolve well in water are not very soluble in nonpolar liquids, while those substances that don't dissolve appreciably in water are often quite soluble in nonpolar solvents. In this experiment, you will take advantage of the differences in solubility between the halogens in molecular form (F_2, Cl_2, Br_2, I_2) and the corresponding halide ions (F^-, Cl^-, Br^-, and I^-). Their charges make the ions very soluble in water, while the molecular halogens are only slightly soluble. By contrast, the molecular halogens are very soluble in nonpolar liquids, but only sparingly so in water.

This experiment will provide you with a chance to compare the relative electron-attracting abilities of the halogens by setting molecular halogens in direct competition for electrons with the ions of other members of their family. Based on tests with certain of the combinations, you should be able to infer the order of relative activities for the entire halogen family.

Safety Precautions

1. Chemical splash-protective eyewear must be worn at all times in the laboratory.

2. **Do not mix ammonia and bleach**; chlorine gas produced by their reaction is highly toxic.

3. Silver nitrate will stain skin and clothing, and is toxic by ingestion. Wash your hands thoroughly before leaving the laboratory. Stains may be removed by washing with sodium thiosulfate solution.

4. The aqueous halogen solutions are toxic and have strong, unpleasant odors. Work only in well-ventilated areas or a fume hood.

5. Hexane and petroleum ether are quite flammable and have strong odors that some people find unpleasant. Use them only where no flames are present and ventilation is good.

6. Petroleum ether and hexane are both extremely volatile. After shaking tubes in Part B, be careful removing the cork. There may well be a spray of liquid.

7. Wash your hands thoroughly before leaving the laboratory.

Materials

Part A

Apparatus

96-well test plate
plastic tooth picks (for stirring)
microtip pipette(s) for mixing
distilled water wash bottle
cotton swabs for cleaning wells

Test Reagents

0.2 M calcium nitrate, $Ca(NO_3)_2$
0.1 M silver nitrate, $AgNO_3$
4 M ammonia solution, NH_3 (aq)
0.2 M sodium thiosulfate, $Na_2S_2O_3$
starch solution
bleach

Halide Ion Solutions:

0.1 M sodium fluoride, NaF
0.1 M sodium chloride, NaCl
0.1 M sodium bromide, NaBr
0.1 M sodium iodide, NaI

Part B

Apparatus

13 x100-mm test tubes
   (at least 4, preferably 6)
24-well test plate or other rack for test tubes
corks for tubes

Reagents

hexane or petroleum ether
iodine solution, I_2(aq)
bromine solution, Br_2(aq)
chlorine solution, Cl_2(aq)
0.2 M NaF(aq)
0.2 M NaCl(aq)
0.2 M NaBr(aq)
0.2 M NaI(aq)
$Na_2S_2O_3$(aq), saturated (for cleanup)

Procedure

Part A: Qualitative Analysis of the Halide Ion Group

Fluoride

1. Obtain labeled thin-stem pipettes containing 0.1 M solutions of NaF, NaCl, NaBr, and NaI.

2. Add 4 drops each of 0.1 M NaF, NaCl, NaBr, and NaI to four separate wells of your well plate.

3. Add 4 drops of 0.2 M calcium nitrate, $Ca(NO_3)_2$, to each well and observe.

Chloride, Bromide and Iodide

4. Add 4 drops each of 0.1 M NaF, NaCl, NaBr, and NaI to four separate wells of your well plate.

5. Add 4 drops of 0.1 M silver nitrate, $AgNO_3$, to each well and observe, making note of both the presence and color of any precipitates that form.

6. Split the precipitates, keeping track of which halide ion is contained in which well. First, agitate the precipitate by placing the tip of the pipette on the bottom of the well, then use a gentle squeeze of air to stir the mixture. (Take everything up into the pipette and then distribute it drop by drop between the original well and another one next to it.)

7. Add 4 drops of 4 M NH_3(aq) to one half of each precipitate, stir with a toothpick, and observe. Does ammonia cause the precipitate to dissolve? Does it cause the precipitate to discolor?

8. Add 4 drops of 0.2 M sodium thiosulfate, $Na_2S_2O_3$, to the second half of each precipitate, stir with a toothpick, and observe. Describe any effect on the precipitates?

9. Add 4 drops each of 0.1 M NaF, NaCl, NaBr, and NaI to four separate wells of your well plate.

10. Add 2 drops of 3% starch solution to each well. Stir and observe.

11. Now add 2 drops of commercial bleach (NaOCl) to each well, stir, and observe again.

Unknowns

12. Obtain an unknown halide ion solution and test with each reagent or combination of reagents, as described above, until the identity of the halide ion present has been determined.

13. Obtain an unknown solution that contains two of the four halide ions mixed together. Test with each reagent or combination of reagents until the identities of both halide ions are known.

Part B: Halogen Activity Series

Notes: 1. Volumes can be estimated here.

2. For convenience, assume that 1 mL = 25 drops from a thin-stem pipette and that a completely full pipette holds 4 mL.

3. While petroleum ether and hexane work equally well, the Procedure assumes hexane.

Preliminary Tests

14. Place 0.5 mL of hexane in each of three test tubes. To one of the tubes add 0.5 mL of chlorine water, Cl_2(aq). Add 0.5 mL of bromine water, Br_2(aq), to the second tube, and place 0.5 mL of iodine water, I_2(aq), in the third. Cork the tubes and shake briefly to mix. Note and record the color and appearance of the contents of each layer in each tube. Record your observations.

Activity Tests

15. Into each of four separate test tubes, place 0.5 mL of one of the four halide ion solutions: NaF, NaCl, NaBr, and NaI. Be sure to keep track of which halide ion is in which tube. Add 0.5 mL of hexane to each tube, followed by 0.25 mL of chlorine water. Cork the tubes and shake briefly to mix. Allow the contents to settle and make note of the appearance of both layers in each tube.

16. Repeat the process, this time substituting bromine water for chlorine water and using NaCl in place of NaBr. Again, describe the results of the tests on fluoride ion, chloride ion, and iodide ion. If you need to reuse the tubes, be sure to clean them out as described below under **Disposal**.

17. Finally, test solutions of fluoride, chloride, and bromide ions with iodine solution, record the results, and complete the **Disposal** procedure.

Disposal

Part A: Qualitative Analysis of the Halide Ion Group

1. While it may be within local regulations to simply rinse all materials down the drain, a more responsible approach is to shake the contents of the well plate onto several thicknesses of paper towel. Once the toweling has dried, it may be safely discarded in the landfill.

Part B: Halogen Activity Series

2. While the halide ion solutions present no chemical hazard, both hexane and the molecular halogens must be disposed of with caution. Add about 1 mL of saturated sodium sulfite solution to each tube. Cork the tube and gently shake it. This will convert the molecular halogens to halide ions and will move them out of the organic layer (hexane) and into the lower, aqueous layer. Consult your teacher concerning further disposal.

3. Use a small brush and warm, soapy water to clean the tubes. Return them to their proper location.

4. Wash your hands thoroughly before leaving the laboratory.

Analysis and Conclusions

Part A: Qualitative Analysis of the Halide Ion Group

1. Describe the information you found from steps 1–11 of this experiment. Make separate clear, concise, and grammatically correct statements for each item. Someone else should be able to take your answers and do the unknowns successfully.

2. Report your results for each of the unknowns. Identify the ion(s) you found and cite the evidence on which your decisions were based. Remember to include the number of your unknowns.

3. In what way does fluoride ion behave differently from the other three ions in the family?

4. In what way(s) do chloride, bromide, and iodide behave similarly? In what way(s) do they display different chemical behavior?

5. Write net ionic equations for the reactions that occurred in steps 1–5 of the procedure. Reactions that took place in later steps will be discussed at the end of this experiment.

6. How can you distinguish between:
   a. Chloride ion and bromide ion?
   b. Chloride ion and iodide ion?
   c. Bromide ion and iodide ion?

7. The re-dissolving of precipitates that you observed in steps 7 and 8 was the result of *complex ion* formation. Silver ion forms such ions with both molecular ammonia, NH_3, and with thiosulfate ion, $S_2O_3{}^{2-}$. With ammonia, it forms the diamminesilver(I) ion,[1] which has the formula $Ag(NH_3)_2{}^+(aq)$. Its complex with thiosulfate is called dithiosulfatoargentate, and has the formula: $Ag(S_2O_3)_2{}^{3-}$. You will notice that, like many of the polyatomic anions that you've seen before, the second one has an -ate ending to its name. The ammonia complex is a cation, so (like metal cations) it has no change in its name ending.

   a. Write net ionic equations for reaction between solid silver chloride, $AgCl(s)$, and:

      i. Aqueous ammonia, to form diammine silver [Hint: and what else?]

      ii. Aqueous thiosulfate ion, to form dithiosulfatoargentate [Same hint.]

   b. The two complexes form because the bonds between silver ion and ammonia or thiosulfate are stronger than the bond holding silver to chloride. Is the bond between silver and bromide ions stronger or weaker than the bonds in the two complex ions? (Hint: You will have to compare them separately.) Defend your answers.

Part B: Halogen Activity Series

8. For those combinations in which reactions were observed, write equations for the reactions that took place. You need not write equations for any cases in which there was no chemical reaction.

9. The equations you have just written are redox reactions. Identify the substance being oxidized and the oxidizing agent in each case.

10. a. Of the three molecular halogens you used, which is the most active? In other words, which one can best convert the others from anionic to molecular form? Cite experimental evidence for your choice.

    b. Examination of your data should let you place bromine, chlorine, and iodine in order of relative activity, which is to say, in order of their abilities to act as oxidizing agents. A more active molecular halogen is able to oxidize (take electrons from) the anion of less-active members of the group. Once you have established the order for these three, you should be able to place fluorine relative to the other three, based on their positions on the periodic table.

11. Suppose you had been provided with a solution of molecular fluorine, $F_2(aq)$. Write net ionic equations for the reactions that you would expect as $F_2(aq)$ is mixed with hexane and solutions of the other halides.

12. It would be impossible for your teacher to prepare an aqueous solution of molecular fluorine. Suggest an explanation for this fact.

---

[1] Or simply, diammine silver.

AP Experimental Chemistry

Experiment 11

Energy Levels and Electron Transitions

Objective

To use colorimetric methods to produce Beer's Law plots for colored transition metal cation solutions, then to use those plots to quantitatively analyze a solution containing one of the cations in an unknown concentration

Concepts

Electromagnetic spectrum, ground and excited states, spectrophotometry, quantitative analysis

Introduction

Already you have seen that many substances, especially transition metal compounds, have very distinctive colors. For example, copper(II) solutions are blue or blue-green; potassium permanganate forms a dark purple solution; and solutions of iron(III) salts, such as iron(III) chloride, are yellow. Perhaps you have been curious as to the source of these colors.

Recall that Bohr's recognition that energy levels for the electrons on atoms were quantized came from the bright-line spectra that each different element exhibited. His interpretation of these spectra was that atoms were absorbing energy and being stimulated from their ground state to some excited (higher energy) state. They then return to the ground state, emitting a photon of electromagnetic energy in the process. The energy of the emitted photon corresponds exactly to the difference in energies between the excited and ground states.

As you know, the transition metal ions have their highest-energy electrons in *d*-orbitals. It turns out that ordinary visible light is able to stimulate some of these *d*-electrons to excited states; the electrons in the *d*-orbitals of transition metal ions absorb certain energies of visible light to make these transitions. Visible light consists of a continuous range of energies; the same continuous spectrum that we know as the "rainbow." Each ion absorbs only those energies that correspond to the energy differences between allowed energy states; all other energies are allowed to pass through, and it is the unabsorbed energies that we see as the color of a solution of transition metal ions. That is, copper(II) solutions appear blue because blue is the color that the Cu^{2+} ions **do not** absorb. What they do absorb is the colors you don't see. If you're familiar with the color wheel and the concept of *complementary colors*, it may interest you to know that these colored solutions absorb colors that are complementary to the colors that they transmit.

As you have learned, visible light is just one portion of the electromagnetic spectrum, which consists of energies ranging from very low, such as radio waves, to very high, such as cosmic radiation. Scientists distinguish among the various energies by referring to the frequency (ν) or wave length (λ) of the wave. In this experiment, we will use the wavelength. The higher the energy of the wave, the higher the frequency will be and the shorter the wavelength will become; in effect, the lower the energy, the more spread-out the wave will be. As an illustration, suppose you tie one end of a rope to a pole, then shake the other end up and down; you've created a *standing wave*. The harder you shake (the more energy you give the wave) the more crests you get in the same space. By increasing the energy, you shorten the length of the wave. Visible light makes up only a tiny portion of the electromagnetic spectrum, ranging from the lowest energy waves, with wavelengths about 700 nanometers (700 nm = 0.000 000 7 m = 7×10^{-7} m), down to wavelengths of about 400 nm for the highest energies.

In this experiment, your class will test solutions of three common transition metal cations: cobalt(II), Co^{2+}, copper(II), Cu^{2+}, and nickel(II), Ni^{2+}. Each solution is distinctly colored. You will test each solution with three different colors of light: red ($\lambda = 635$ nm), green ($\lambda = 590$ nm), and blue ($\lambda = 470$ nm), to see which color is most strongly absorbed by each one. You will also vary the concentration of the ion solutions to see how the amount of light absorbed varies with the amount of the metal ion that is present. Not surprisingly, the extent to which light of a given wavelength is absorbed varies linearly with the molar concentration of the absorbing species (here, the cation being tested). The relationship between concentration and absorption is known as the Beer-Lambert Law, or simply Beer's Law. You might want to read about it, either in advance or as you begin the write-up of the experiment. You will make a Beer's Law plot, using standards of known concentration, then you will use your plot to determine the concentration of an unknown solution of the same cation.

This is potentially quite a long experiment, requiring about $2^1/_2$ hours for completion to do the entire procedure for all three metal cations. For that reason, your teacher will assign different metals to different groups or individuals. The process is the same for all three of the cation solutions, so all lab groups will be doing the same thing. Each person on the lab team will also be assigned a solution containing "their" cation, but in an unknown concentration. These will not have the concentrations of the five standards, but will fall in between your data points. From the plot of absorbance versus concentration, that concentration is to be determined.

Prelaboratory Assignment

Read the entire experiment before you begin.

Prelaboratory Questions

1. Write the electron configurations for the ions involved in this experiment:
    a. cobalt(II)   b. copper(II)   c. nickel(II)

2. Explain the difference between ground states and excited states for atoms.

3. Starting with 0.50 M stock solution, describe the process by which you could make 10.0 mL each of 0.40 M, 0.30 M, 0.20 M, and 0.10 M nickel(II) nitrate.

Safety Precautions

1. Chemical splash-protective eyewear must be worn at all times in the laboratory.

2. The cobalt solution is mildly toxic and a suspected carcinogen in high concentrations. (0.50 M is not considered "high concentration.")

3. Nickel(II) nitrate is mildly toxic and a known carcinogen in high concentrations.

4. Wash your hands thoroughly with soap and water before leaving the laboratory.

Materials

Apparatus

colorimeter probe and interface
    or spectrophotometer
cuvettes for colorimeter (5)
beakers, 30–50 mL (5, if possible)
Mohr (graduated) pipettes, 10-mL (2)
beaker for discarding solutions, 100-mL or larger

Reagents

nickel(II) nitrate, $Ni(NO_3)_2$(aq), 0.50 M
cobalt(II) nitrate, $Co(NO_3)_2$(aq), 0.50 M
copper(II) nitrate, $Cu(NO_3)_2$(aq), 0.50 M
distilled water (wash bottle)

Procedure

1. A typical colorimeter apparatus is shown in the figure below. It is connected to an interface, such as CBL2, LabPro, LabQuest, etc. If you are using a different type of device, such as a self-contained spectrophotometer, your teacher will instruct you in its operation. The principle of operation is straightforward. The intensity of light of a given wavelength that passes through a solution is measured. This %T (percent transmittance) is converted by the electronics of the device into a property called absorbance. Your text has an extended discussion of the process, with much greater detail.

2. Obtain about 20 mL of 0.50 *M* solution of the cation assigned to you. Using one Mohr pipet for the cation solution and the other for distilled water, carefully prepare 10 mL each of 0.40 *M*, 0.30 *M*, 0.20 *M*, and 0.10 *M* solutions of your cation. **Important:** the greater the care with which you prepare these solutions, the better your results will be, the more linear your three graphs will appear, and the more useful they will be for determination of the unknown's concentration.

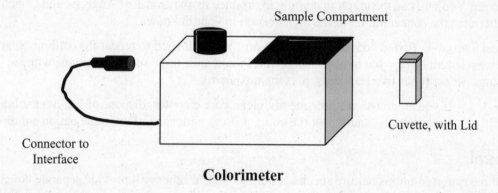

Colorimeter

3. If your colorimeter is not a stand-alone device, make the connections to a graphing calculator or computer as your teacher directs. Set it to record absorbances when told to do so, rather than continuously.

   Note 1: Cuvettes for most interface devices are square, with two ribbed sides and two smooth sides. When handling such cuvettes, touch only the ribbed sides and always wipe the outside of the cuvette with a lint-free tissue before placing it in the colorimeter. Never place a cuvette that is wet on the outside into the colorimeter chamber.

   Note 2: Spectrophotometers use test-tube-like tubes in place of cuvettes. They too must be wiped with a lint-free tissue before being inserted in the sampling chamber. They also must be inserted so that a mark on the tube coincides with a mark on the sampling chamber.

4. Turn the colorimeter on, allow it to warm up if necessary, then carry out the calibration process (if needed), as instructed by your teacher. In essence, the calibration makes a record of how much light passes through the cuvette if there is 100% transmission (Absorbance = 0) and if there is 0% transmission (100% absorbance). You are now ready to run your five samples of known concentrations, as well as your unknown. Calibrate it first at the shortest wavelength, 470 nm. You will have to repeat the calibration for each of the other two wavelengths.

5. Rinse a clean cuvette twice using approximately 1 mL of 0.10 *M* solution, discarding the rinsings into your waste beaker. Fill the cuvette at least $^3/_4$ full of 0.10 *M* solution, replace the cap and carefully wipe the outside with a lint-free wipe. Replace the blank (distilled water) cuvette with the one containing the 0.1 *M* solution. With the wavelength setting still on 470 nm, wait for the reading to become steady, then tell the instrument to record the absorbance. If you are prompted

to enter the concentration, enter 0.10 (or 0.1); this tells the interface that the absorbance it just measured is for a 0.10 M solution.

Important: Remove the cuvette from the sample holder and place it where you can easily identify it for later use; you will need it two more times.

6. Repeat Step 5 four more times, using separate cuvettes (if available) for the 0.20-, 0.30-, 0.40-, and 0.50-M solutions. Be sure to place each cuvette where it can be easily identified for reuse.

When you have completed all five samples, stop data collection. Depending on the interface you are using, it will probably plot your data, but may not draw a line through the points. Copy the data from the interface into your notebook, in the form of a table. Be sure to head the table with the identity of the cation and the wavelength of light that was used.

7. You will be provided with a solution of your cation in an unknown concentration. Determine the absorbance of your unknown by placing a cuvette containing the unknown into the sampling chamber. You will use the graph that you will produce in question 1 of Analysis and Conclusions to determine the concentration of the metal cation in your unknown.

8. Repeat Steps 4–8, first at 565 nm, then at 635 nm. You will need to repeat the calibration at each new wavelength. When you have finished, you should have three sets of readings, with six readings per set (your five standards, plus the unknown).

Note 3:   If you are to use all three metals, clean your cuvettes, dispose of left-over solutions appropriately, and repeat the entire process with each of the other cation solutions.

Disposal

1. All three cation solutions require special handling. Your teacher will provide separate collection vessels for each of the three cation waste solutions. Empty any remaining solution from beakers and cuvettes into your waste beaker and transfer it to the appropriate collection vessel.

2. Gently wash the cuvettes in soapy water, then rinse thoroughly with distilled water. Unless your teacher directs you otherwise, leave them to dry, mouth down, on paper towel. Clean the caps in the same fashion.

3. Follow your teacher's instructions regarding what is to be done with the interface, the colorimeter probe, and any connectors that were used.

Analysis and Conclusions

1. On a single set of axes, plot the data for all three wavelengths, with Absorbance (A) on the vertical axis and concentration on the horizontal axis. To help distinguish among the three, place the points inside different shapes; for example, △ and ⊙. Draw the best straight-line fit through each set of points.

2. What color of light does your metal cation absorb most strongly? This wavelength of maximum absorbance is often referred to as λ_{max} ("lambda-max"), where the Greek letter λ (lambda), stands for wavelength.

3. Based on your own results or on those of others in the class, which of the metals shows its maximum absorbance at the longest wavelength? At the shortest wavelength?

4. Using the plot for your metal at its wavelength of maximum absorbance:

   a. Estimate the absorbance of a 0.33 M solution.

   b. Estimate the concentration of a solution that has an absorbance of 0.100 at its λ_{max}.

5. Based on its absorbance at its particular value of λ_{max}, estimate the concentration of your unknown. Briefly discuss the limitations on the precision of your estimate, including how well the concentration at λ_{max} compares with those obtained for your unknown at other wavelengths.

6. The frequency of a wave is the number of waves or pulses that passes a given point in a certain length of time. When the frequency is measured in (waves) per second, the units are s^{-1}, also known as Hertz, and abbreviated Hz. A wave whose frequency is 100 megahertz, 100 MHz, is sending out 100,000,000 pulses every second!

   Recall the rope-wave illustration in the Introduction to this experiment: the greater the frequency, the shorter the wavelength. From the preceding, it must follow that the higher the energy of a photon of light, the shorter the wavelength associated with it. Which of the metals has electrons making the greatest energy change as the result of absorption of light? Defend your answer.

7. Read the discussion of Beer's Law plots in your text. Consider the equation $A = \varepsilon\, l\, c$, where A is absorbance, l is the path length (the distance the light travels through your solution), and c is the solution concentration.

   a. Assuming that the path length for the colorimeter you just used is 1.5 cm, determine the molar extinction coefficient, ε, of your metal cation.

   b. Rearrange the equation to show why the graph you drew should have a constant slope. Include a written explanation as part of your response.

Experiment 12

The Percentage of Copper in Brass
A Colorimetric Determination

Objective

To determine the mass percent of copper in a sample of brass

Concepts

Quantitative analysis, oxidation-reduction, spectrophotometry

Introduction

The unique properties of metals arise because the atoms pack closely together and share their highest-energy electrons with all their neighbors. At the atomic level, a metal can be thought of as an array of positive nuclei surrounded by a sea of mobile electrons. These mobile electrons conduct heat and electricity through the metallic structures. Metals bond equally well in all directions. This permits metals to bend, because strong directional bonds do not have to break. All elements (except hydrogen, and there is some recent evidence for even hydrogen[1]) on the left-hand side of the periodic table exist as metals when pure.

Often it is possible to mix different metallic elements simply by melting them together. Upon cooling, the mixture produces a new mixed metal called an *alloy*. The percentages of the metals can be varied somewhat to customize the properties of the alloys. Brass was one of the first alloys produced and typically contains somewhere between 67–90% copper and 33–10% zinc. Copper is too soft to be useful in its pure state and zinc's melting point is too low to let it serve as a building material. But brass has mechanical properties that make it superior to both copper and zinc.

In this experiment to determine the percentage of copper in a sample of brass, you will first dissolve the brass in nitric acid solution. The resulting blue solution of copper(II) ion will then be compared to solutions of known concentration, both visually and by means of a Beer's Law plot, to determine the concentration of copper(II) ion in the solution.

Prelaboratory Assignment

Read the entire experiment before you begin.

Prelaboratory Questions

1. What are alloys? How are they similar to more familiar combinations such as salt water and air? How are alloys different from these more-common mixtures?

2. Write the balanced molecular and net-ionic equations for the reaction between copper metal and nitric acid. Assume the products are copper(II) nitrate, gaseous nitrogen monoxide, and liquid water. Are there any spectator ions in this system? Explain.

3. As explained in the Introduction, the copper content of typical brass samples can vary widely, but generally is in the neighborhood of 75% by mass, assuming you are using 0.30 g of an alloy that is exactly 90.% copper by mass:

   a. Determine the mass and number of moles of copper that will be present in your sample.

---

[1] But the conditions needed to observe metallic hydrogen are on the order of 10^6 K and several thousand atmospheres.

   b. Determine the number of moles of nitric acid needed to completely react with the number of moles of copper that you just calculated.

   c. Determine the volume of 6.0 *M* nitric acid that will be needed to completely consume all of the copper in your hypothetical brass sample. Express your answer in milliliters, mL.

4. The actual volume of nitric acid that you use is likely to be significantly larger than what you calculated in **3c**. Why might an excess of acid be helpful in this determination?

5. If your sample of brass as described in question 3 (0.30 g, 90.% Cu) is used to make 10.0 mL of solution, what will be the concentration of copper(II) ion in your solution?

Safety Precautions

1. Chemical splash-protective eyewear must be worn at all times in the laboratory.

2. 6 *M* nitric acid is a strong skin and eye irritant. When spilled on the skin, nitric acid causes a yellow stain followed by a burn. Wash with water immediately after exposure.

3. Copper solutions are toxic. Avoid contact with skin. Wash hands thoroughly before leaving the laboratory.

Materials

Apparatus

Sample Preparation
beaker, 30—50 mL for dissolving sample
balance, milligram sensitivity
volumetric flask, 10-mL

Analysis, Method A
24-well test plate
thin-stem plastic pipettes (2)
beaker for discarding solutions, 100-mL or larger

Analysis, Method B
colorimeter probe and interface
cuvettes for colorimeter (5, if possible)
beakers, 30–50 mL (5, if possible)
Mohr (graduated) pipets, 10-mL (2)
beaker for discarding solutions, 100-mL or larger

Reagents

brass sample
nitric acid, 6 *M*, HNO$_3$(*aq*)

copper(II) nitrate, Cu(NO$_3$)$_2$(*aq*), 0.50 *M*
distilled water (wash bottle)

Procedure

Part 1: Preparation of the Sample

1. Weigh out, accurately, about 0.3 g (± 1 mg) of well-cleaned brass alloy in a small beaker.

2. Place the beaker in a fume hood and add 20 drops of 6 *M* HNO$_3$.

3. When the reaction slows add an additional 20 drops of acid. Repeat until all the brass dissolves. It may help to warm the beaker gently on a small hotplate.

   Note: **Do not** leave the beaker unattended on the hotplate. You have only a very small volume of liquid, which will evaporate rapidly to dryness.

4. Using a transfer pipette, move all the copper solution to a 10-mL volumetric flask. Rinse your beaker with three 1-mL portions of distilled water; transfer these rinsings to your volumetric flask. Add water to make the volume exactly 10.00 mL. Stopper the flask and invert it many times to be sure the solution is completely mixed. Use your solution for each of the following analysis methods.

Analysis Method A: Visual Analysis

1. Fill the A and C rows of your well plate with the following combinations of 0.50 M copper(II) nitrate solution and distilled water. (Row B will be used for your brass solution.) Note that each well will have a total of 40 drops of liquid.

Well	A1	A2	A3	A4	A5	A6
Drops 0.50 M Cu(NO$_3$)$_2$	8	10	12	14	16	18
Drops distilled water	32	30	28	26	24	22

Well	C1	C2	C3	C4	C5	C6
Drops 0.50 M Cu(NO$_3$)$_2$	20	22	24	26	28	30
Drops distilled water	20	18	16	14	12	10

Add 40 drops of your copper solution from the brass to wells B2 and B4. Compare the color intensity of your solution with those in rows A and C. You may find it helpful to place your copper solution in one or more other wells of row B to help with the color-matching process. When you have a color match, determine the concentration of copper in your brass sample, following the directions given in questions 2 and 3 of Analysis and Conclusions.

Analysis Method B: Beer's Law Curve

2. A typical colorimeter apparatus is shown in the figure below. It is connected to an interface, such as CBL2, LabPro, LabQuest, etc. If you are using a different tool, such as a spectrophotometer, your teacher will instruct you in its operation. The principle of operation is straightforward. The intensity of light of a given wavelength that passes through a solution is measured. This %T (percent transmittance) is converted by the electronics of the device into a property called absorbance. Your text has an extended discussion of the process, with much greater detail.

3. Obtain about 20 mL of 0.50 M solution of copper(II) nitrate. Using distilled water and your two Mohr pipets, carefully prepare 10 mL each of 0.40 M, 0.30 M, 0.20 M, and 0.10 M solutions.

    Important: the greater the care with which you prepare these solutions, the better your results will be, the better your graph will look, and the more accurate your results will be.

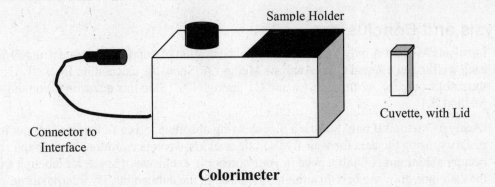

Colorimeter

AP Experimental Chemistry

4. If your colorimeter is not a stand-alone device, make the connections to a graphing calculator or computer as your teacher directs. Set it to record absorbances when told to do so, rather than continuously.

    Note 1:   Cuvettes for most interface devices are square, with two ribbed sides and two smooth sides. When handling such cuvettes, touch only the ribbed sides and always wipe the outside of the cuvette with a lint-free tissue before placing it in the colorimeter. Never place a cuvette that is wet on the outside in the colorimeter.

    Note 2:   Spectrophotometers use test-tube-like tubes in place of cuvettes. They too must be wiped with a lint-free tissue before being inserted in the sampling chamber. They also must be inserted so that a mark on the tube coincides with a mark on the sampling chamber.

5. Turn the colorimeter on, allow it to warm up if necessary, then carry out the calibration process at 635 nm, as instructed by your teacher. In essence, the calibration makes a record of how much light passes through the cuvette when there is 100% transmission (Absorbance = 0) and when there is 0% transmission (100% absorbance). You are now ready to run your five samples of known concentrations, as well as the solution prepared from your brass sample.

6. Rinse a clean cuvette twice using approximately 1 mL of 0.10 M solution each time, discarding the rinsings into your waste beaker. Fill the cuvette at least ¾ full of 0.10 M solution, replace the cap, and carefully wipe the outside with a lint-free wipe. Replace the blank (distilled water) cuvette with the one containing the 0.1 M solution. With the wavelength set at 635 nm, wait for the reading to become steady, then tell the instrument to record the absorbance. If you are prompted to enter the concentration, enter 0.10 (or 0.1); this tells the interface that the absorbance it just measured is for a 0.10 M solution. Set the cuvette aside, in case you need to use it again.

7. Repeat the previous step four more times, using 0.20 M, 0.30 M, 0.40 M, and 0.50 M $Cu(NO_3)_2$. As before, if your colorimeter prompts you to do so, enter the appropriate concentrations for each, then set them aside in case they are needed again. Be sure you keep track of which is which.

8. Finally, fill a clean cuvette with some of your unknown brass solution. Manually record the value shown (either for %T or A) in your notebook, but *do not enter a concentration value*. If your colorimeter is going to plot the data for you, you don't want this point to appear on your graph.

9. When you have completed all five samples plus the brass solution, stop data collection. The interface will likely display a plot of absorbance (A) versus concentration (c). Whether or not the device makes the A vs c plot for you, you will need to make such a plot in your laboratory notebook, or using a computer program such as Excel™. This plot should be a straight line, showing that absorbance increases linearly with concentration. Check to be certain you recorded the absorbance readings correctly. Present the data into your notebook in the form of a table.

Analysis and Conclusions

1. **a.**   (Analysis Method A only.) Calculate the concentration of copper(II) nitrate, $Cu(NO_3)_2$, in each well in rows A and C for Analysis Method A. Show the calculation for well A1; report the results only for A2 through A6 and C1 through C6. (Skip this question if you did only Method B.)

    b.   (Analysis Method B only.) Make a plot showing absorbance as a function of copper ion molarity, using the data for your five solutions of known concentration. Your graph should occupy a minimum of half a page in your notebook, exclusive of space for labeling axes. Plot the data then draw the best-fit straight line through the data points. By interpolation, graphically determine the copper ion concentration that would correspond to the absorbance value for your unknown.

2. Use the molarity of Cu^{2+}(aq) in your brass solution to determine the number of moles of copper that must have been in the 10.0 mL solution you made from your piece of brass. Convert this number of moles to a mass in grams. If you did both Method A and Method B, show separate calculations for each.

3. From the mass(es) of copper just determined and the mass of your original brass sample, calculate the mass percentage of copper in the brass alloy.

4. Nitric acid was used in this experiment because (as you know from earlier experiments) copper is not oxidized by the hydrogen ions in ordinary mineral acids, such as hydrochloric acid or sulfuric acid. Zinc, on the other hand, will react with hydrochloric and sulfuric acids.

   a. Write the balanced equation for the single-replacement reaction that occurs between zinc metal and hydrochloric acid. (You should be able to predict the products yourself.)

   b. Write the equation for the reaction that occurs between zinc and nitric acid in two different ways.

      i. Assume the products are zinc nitrate and hydrogen gas, similar to what happens with HCl.

      ii. Assume the products are zinc nitrate, nitrogen monoxide gas, and water vapor, as with copper and nitric acid.

   c. Hydrochloric and nitric acids are both monoprotic (each has only one hydrogen ion). How do the mole ratios of acid to zinc compare? How would you decide experimentally which of the two reaction pathways is actually followed?

5. Speculate as to what would happen if a piece of brass were immersed in 6 M HCl(aq). Would you expect the zinc in the brass to react, leaving the copper behind? Explain.

Experiment 13

Molecular Geometry and VSEPR

Objective

To draw Lewis structures and sketch the shapes of several molecules and ions

Concepts

Lewis structures, hybrid orbitals, VSEPR

Introduction

The *octet rule*, first identified by G. N. Lewis in 1902, recognizes the fact that most atoms, especially those known as the "representative elements," bond in such a way as to surround themselves with eight electrons. He further observed that these eight electrons were clustered into four pairs. Today we understand why: the four pairs of electrons correspond to the valence configuration ns^2np^6, which is characteristic of the noble gases (except He). These four pairs of electrons are mutually repelling; that is, they align themselves as far apart as possible. This desire for maximum separation leads to specific shapes for molecules. We have a name for this phenomenon: it is called the *Valence Shell Electron Pair Repulsion* theory, or VSEPR for short.

Another principle involved in this lab is the concept of *valence*. Today we talk about valence levels of atoms and distinguish between an atom's valence and core electrons. But the term valence goes back much farther and refers to *the bonding capacity of the elements*. (Bonding capacity is another term for the number of bonds the atom typically forms and was the source of the group numbers assigned to the various elements by Mendeleev.) The bonding capacity—valence—of the alkali metals is 1; they all form one bond. The same is true of the halogens, in binary compounds at least. The oxygen family generally forms two bonds and the nonmetal members of the nitrogen family typically form three bonds in binary compounds.

In this exercise you will build models of some simple compounds and ions, noting similarities and differences among them. Then you will seek explanations for any patterns that emerge. From your study of Lewis structures, you know that the atoms in molecules often have pairs of electrons that are not involved in the bonding; they are known as *lone pairs*. Lone pairs attached to the perimeter atoms have no effect on the overall shape of the molecule. As you will see, however, lone pairs on the central atom can greatly influence both the shape and the bond angles between atoms.

You will be provided with a set of molecular models in which variously-colored spheres represent the different atom centers, while bonds are shown by short, rigid connectors. The longer, more flexible connectors (springs, in some sets) are used for making double bonds. None of the structures called for here involve triple bonds. Lone pairs on the central atom will be indicated by lobe-shaped pieces.

For each item in Part A you are to start with the Lewis structure of the molecule or ion, construct it, and sketch its 3-dimensional shape. Your drawing should indicate bond angles, taking into account the effect of lone pairs (e.g., the lone pair on NH_3 reduces the angle between N—H bonds from 109.5° to about 107°).

Once the model has been drawn, you are to name the shape of the molecule. (Hint: remember that the shape is determined only by the relative positions of the central atom and the perimeter atoms.)

Where more than one arrangement is possible, build and draw both (or all) possibilities, then explain which is the more likely to occur, and why. These different arrangements are called *isomers*. In some cases, one isomer is more likely than another, but not always, as you will see in Part B.

Finally, you will group your structures into categories based on the number of perimeter atoms and the number of lone (nonbonding) electron pairs on the central atom. These are referred to as "A–X–E" categories, where A represents the central atom, the Xs are the perimeter atoms, and E refers to any lone pairs on the central atom. (Lone pairs on perimeter atoms are ignored, since they have no role in determining the shape of the molecule or ion.) Thus, a molecule in which the central atom has three atoms attached and one lone pair would be described as AX_3E. If there are no lone pairs on the central atom, E is not used. CH_4 is simply AX_4. Your experiment and report will probably take the better part of two hours. The best idea is to answer the questions as you work your way through the procedure. If you just jot notes as you go, you will find it very difficult to do the descriptions later; it's much easier to do everything while the model is in front of you. Working with a partner helps, but you need to stay on track and you both will need to have completed the prelaboratory assignment ahead of time.

Prelaboratory Assignment

1. Read the entire experiment before coming to the laboratory.

2. In you laboratory notebook, draw the Lewis structures for all of the species in Part A of the Procedure. Leave enough space by each one to sketch the models you will build.

Safety Precautions

If you are performing this experiment in the laboratory, chemical splash-protective eyewear must be worn. If not, there are no real safety hazards involved in this experiment, but it is easy to lose the small spheres and connectors. Work on a level surface, if possible, and check around your work area periodically.

Materials

Molecular model kit

Procedure

Part A: Fundamental Structures

1. Build models of each of the species, then sketch the model in your notebook in the space near its Lewis structure. Remember that "electron pair," as it is used here, can refer to a single, double, or triple bond. Carbon dioxide, CO_2, has one effective pair for each of its two double bonds, hence two electron pairs.

2. Categorize each species according to the A–X–E system described in the Introduction. According to this system, CO_2 would be AX_2, but SO_2 is AX_2E because of the lone pair on the sulfur atom.

No. of Electron Pairs	Type of Hybrid Orbitals	Structures
2	sp	CO_2, $BeCl_2$, N_3^- (the azide ion), SO_2^{2+} (the thionyl ion)
3	sp^2	BCl_3, SO_3, NO_3^-, SO_2, NO_2^-
4	sp^3	CH_4, SiF_4, SO_4^{2-} (ignore formal charges), NH_3, PO_3^{3-}, H_2O, SCl_2
5	dsp^3	PCl_5, $TeCl_4$, ClF_3, I_3^- (triiodide ion)
6	d^2sp^3	SF_6, IF_5, XeF_4, IF_4^-

Suggestion: To represent the 3-D structures derived from dsp^3 and d^2sp^3 hybridization, use the sketch forms shown to the right.

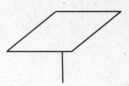

Part B: Additional Structures

3. Draw the Lewis structure, and build and sketch PCl_4^+ and PCl_6^-. To what A–X–E category does each of these ions belong?

4. Draw the Lewis structure, and build and sketch a model of ethane, C_2H_6. How would you describe the shape of this molecule?

5. **a.** Make and sketch $AsCl_5$. Is this molecule polar? Explain.

   b. Now replace one of the chlorine atoms with a fluorine atom using a different color sphere. There are two possible arrangements for this molecule, $AsCl_4F$, both of which are equally likely to exist. Because everything except the placement of the perimeter atoms is the same, they are isomers (see the Introduction), specifically *stereoisomers*.

      Draw them both. Is either or both of the isomers polar? Use your sketches to justify your answer.

   c. Finally, replace a second chlorine "atom" with another fluorine. Now there are three possible stereoisomers; draw 3-dimensional structures for all three isomers of $AsCl_3F_2$. What sort of experimental evidence would help to distinguish among the three isomers? Use your structures to explain how at least one of the three could be distinguished from the other two.

Analysis and Conclusions

1. Because the model kits can't make a tetrahedral structure with two double bonds and two single bonds, you were directed to ignore formal charge considerations for the sulfate ion. What difference would it make to the A–X–E classification and to the structure if you could take formal charge into account?

2. Consider the species CO, N_2, CN^-, and C_2^{2-}. What must be the shape of each, and why? Draw Lewis structures for each and describe the types of hybrid bonding involved for each atom. Finally, draw MO diagrams for each. How does the net bond order from the MO diagram reflect the Lewis structures that you drew?

3. If you were asked to apply the traditional definition of valence to the noble gases, what value would you assign to them? Why would that be considered the valence for that family? Beginning in the late 1950s, chemists successfully produced compounds combining the larger noble gases with very reactive atoms, such as fluorine and oxygen. The first two such compounds were XeF_4 and XeO_3. What must be the explanation for the formation of these compounds? Draw the Lewis structure, build and sketch XeO_3, and identify its A–X–E classification. Do the same for XeF_4.

   Suggest an explanation for the fact that no compound of helium or neon has ever been produced, and none is expected to be made in the future.

Experiment 14

Thin-Layer Chromatography

Objective

To perform a separation of a mixture of colored organic dyes by thin-layer chromatography and to investigate the effect of varying solvent composition on the effectiveness of the separation

Concepts

Solubility, polarity, qualitative and quantitative analysis

Introduction

The word **chromatography** means "color writing." The name was chosen at the beginning of the 20th century when the method was first used to separate colored components from plant leaves. Over the years, chromatography in its various forms has emerged as one of the most important known methods for the chemical analysis of mixtures.

The earliest form of chromatography, paper chromatography, was performed using ordinary filter paper, which consists primarily of the polymeric carbohydrate cellulose, as the medium upon which the mixture to be separated is applied. The more modern technique of **thin-layer chromatography** (universally abbreviated as **TLC**) uses a thin coating of aluminum oxide (alumina) or silica gel on a glass microscope slide or plastic sheet. The mixture to be resolved is applied to the slide or sheet, then a solvent mixture is allowed to pass through the sample mixture.

In TLC, a single drop or spot of the unknown mixture to be analyzed is placed about half an inch from the end of a TLC slide. The TLC slide is then placed in a shallow layer of solvent mixture in a jar or beaker. Since the coating of the TLC slide is permeable to liquids, the solvent begins *rising* through the coating by capillary action.

As the solvent rises to the level at which the spot of mixture was applied, various effects can occur, depending on the constituents of the spot. Those components of the spot that are completely soluble in the solvent will be swept along with the solvent front as it continues to rise. Components that are not at all soluble in the solvent will be left behind at the original location of the spot. Most components of the unknown spot mixture will lie in between these extremes and will be carried along by the solvent front, but to *different extents* reflecting their specific solubilities, allowing them to separate as the solvent front passes. In this way, the original spot of mixture is spread out into a series of spots or bands, with each spot representing one single component of the original mixture.

The separation of a mixture by chromatography is not solely a function of the solubilities of the components in the solvent used, however. The TLC slide coating used in chromatography is not entirely inert to the molecules in the mixture. To one extent or another, the coating material on the slide surface may interact with the molecules of the components of the mixture being separated. Each component of the mixture is likely to have a different extent of interaction with the slide coating. This difference in interaction between the components of a mixture and the support medium forms an equally important basis for the separation. The coating of the TLC slide adsorbs[1] molecules on its surface to differing extents, depending on the structure and properties of the molecules involved.

---

[1] A*d*sorb means to stick to the outer surface, as opposed to being a*b*sorbed into a substance.

AP Experimental Chemistry

In order to quantify a TLC separation, a mathematical function called the **retention factor**, R_f, is defined by the relationship shown as follows.

$$R_f = \frac{\text{distance travelled by spot}}{\text{distance travelled by solvent}}$$

The retention factor depends on what solvent is used for the separation and on the composition of the slide coating used for a particular analysis. Because the retention factors for particular components of a mixture may vary if an analysis is repeated under different conditions, a *known* sample is generally analyzed at the *same time* as an *unknown* mixture on the same TLC slide. If the unknown mixture produces spots having the same R_f values as spots from the known sample, then an identification of the unknown components has been achieved.

Thin-layer chromatography is only one example of the many different chromatographic methods available. Mixtures of volatile liquids are commonly separated by *gas chromatography*, in which the mixture of liquids is vaporized and passed through a long tube of solid adsorbent material that has been coated with an appropriate liquid. The mixture is pushed along by the action of a carrier gas (usually one that is chemically inert, such as helium). As with TLC, the components of the mixture will have different solubilities in the liquid coating and different attractions for the solid adsorbent material. Separation of the components of the mixture occurs as the mixture progresses through the tube. The mixture components exit the tube one by one and are usually detected by electronic means.

In this experiment, you will perform a thin-layer chromatographic analysis of a mixture of the dyes bromcresol green, methyl red, and malachite green. These dyes have been chosen because they have significantly different retention factors, so a nearly complete separation should be possible in the appropriate solvent system. Often the components of a mixture are difficult or impossible to detect with the naked eye, so the TLC slide is coated with a fluorescent indicator. The dyes selected for this experiment have intense, distinct colors, so no special indicator is needed. The chromatographic separation will be attempted in several solvent mixtures to investigate which solvent mixture gives the most complete resolution of the three dyes.

In actual practice, thin-layer chromatography has several uses. When a new compound is synthesized, for example, a TLC of the new compound is routinely done to make certain that the new compound is pure (a completely pure compound should only give a single TLC spot; impurities would result in additional spots). TLC is also used to separate the components of natural mixtures isolated from biological systems: for example, the various pigments in plants can be separated by TLC of an extract made by boiling the plant leaves in a solvent. Once the components of a mixture have been separated by TLC, it is even possible to isolate small quantities of each component by scraping its spot from the TLC slide and re-dissolving the spot in some suitable solvent.

Prelaboratory Assignment

Read the entire experiment before you begin.

Prelaboratory Questions

1. What are the two basic factors that lead to separation of mixtures by thin-layer chromatography?

2. Identify at least two methods other than chromatography that involve separating the components of a mixture based on solubility differences.

3. There are four liquids that make up the solvent mixtures that you will use. They are: acetone (CH_3COCH_3), ethanol (CH_3CH_2OH), ethyl acetate ($CH_3COOCH_2CH_3$), and hexane (C_6H_{14}). Draw the Lewis structures for each one and rank them in what you would expect to be the order of increasing polarity. Defend (give reasons for) your rankings. (Hint: You may need to consult your text or some other reference for help with the structures.)

4. You are instructed to wear plastic gloves when preparing the TLC materials for this experiment. Aside from reasons of safety and health, why are gloves needed?

Safety Precautions

1. Chemical splash-protective eyewear must be worn at all times in the laboratory.

2. The organic indicator dyes used in this experiment will stain skin and clothing. Many such dyes are toxic or mutagenic.

3. The solvents used for the chromatographic separation are highly flammable and their vapors are toxic. No flames are allowed in the room while these solvents are in use. Work only in a fume hood or an exceptionally well-ventilated area.

4. Dispose of the solvents in the appropriate waste container. Under no circumstances are they to be poured down the drain.

Materials

Apparatus

beakers, 400 mL or larger (6)
plastic TLC slides (~4 x 10 cm)
latex surgical gloves
ruler
pencil
plastic wrap or Parafilm®
10-microliter (10 µL) micropipets
    or melting point capillary tubes, unsealed

Reagents

Ethanolic solutions of the indicator dyes:
    methyl red
    malachite green
    bromcresol green
Solvent mixtures: combinations of:
    acetone, CH_3COCH_3
    ethanol, CH_3CH_2OH
    ethyl acetate, $CH_3COOCH_2CH_3$
    hexane, C_6H_{14}

Procedure

1. Clean and dry six 200-mL beakers to be used as the chambers for the chromatography and six squares of plastic wrap or Parafilm® to be used as covers for the beakers.

2. Place a small volume of each solvent into separate beakers, to a depth of about 0.5 cm. The mixtures to be used are listed below. Cover the beakers after adding the solvent mixture, and label the beakers with the identity of the mixture each contains.

    acetone 60% / hexane 40%   ethyl acetate 60% / hexane 40%

    acetone 50% / ethyl acetate 50%   acetone 50% / ethanol 50%

    ethyl acetate 50% / ethanol 50%   hexane 50% / ethanol 50%

3. Wearing plastic surgical gloves to avoid any oils transferring from your fingers to the slides, prepare 6 plastic TLC slides by marking *lightly* with pencil (not ink) a line across both the top and bottom of the slide. Do not mark the line too deeply or you will remove the coating of the slide. On one of the lines you have drawn on each slide, mark four small pencil dots (to represent where the spots are to be applied). *Above* the other line on each slide, mark the following letters: R (methyl *r*ed), M (*m*alachite green), G (bromcresol *g*reen), and X (mixture). See Figure 14-1.

4. The spots can be applied using either a 10-μL pipet or by simply dipping a glass melting-point capillary tube into the dye mixture, then touching the tip of the capillary to the slide. Obtain small samples of the ethanolic solutions of the three dyes (methyl red, malachite green, and bromcresol green). Also obtain 4 micropipets: use a separate micropipet or capillary for each dye, as well as a separate one for the mixture. Be careful not to mix up the pipets during application of the dyes.

Figure 14-1. Plastic TLC slide with spots of the three dyes and the mixture applied.
Keep the spots you apply as small as possible.

5. The spots can be applied using either a 10-μL pipet or by simply dipping a glass melting-point capillary tube into the dye mixture, then touching the tip of the capillary to the slide. Obtain small samples of the ethanolic solutions of the three dyes (methyl red, malachite green, and bromcresol green). Also obtain four micropipets: use a separate micropipet or capillary for each dye, as well as a separate one for the mixture. Be careful not to mix up the pipets during application of the dyes.

6. Apply a single small droplet of the appropriate dye to its pencil spot on each of the TLC slides you have prepared (wipe the outside of the micropipet if necessary before applying the drop to remove any excess dye solution). Keep the spots of dye as small as possible.

7. Apply one droplet of each dye to the spot labeled M (mixture) on each slide, *being sure to allow each previous spot to dry before applying the next dye.* Allow the spots on the TLC slides to dry before proceeding.

Gently lower one of the TLC slides, spots downward, into one of the solvent systems. Be careful not to wet the spots or to slosh the solvent in the beaker; do not move or otherwise disturb the beaker after adding the TLC slide. Carefully cover the beaker with plastic wrap.

Allow the solvent to rise on the TLC slide until it reaches the upper pencil line (this will not take very long, about 10–15 minutes). When the solvent has risen to the upper pencil mark, remove the TLC slide and quickly mark the exact location of the solvent front before it evaporates. Mark the TLC slide with the identity of the solvent system used for development. Set the TLC slide aside to dry completely.

8. Repeat the process using the remaining TLC slides and solvent systems. You can easily have more than one system, even all six, going at the same time. But if you do, be sure you mark each slide with the solvent system used as you remove each from its development chamber.

9. Determine R_f for each dye in each solvent system and record the values in your notebook. Which solvent system led to the most complete resolution of the dye mixture? If no mixture gave a complete resolution, your teacher may suggest other solvents for you to try, or other proportions of the solvents already used. Save your TLC slides and staple them to the lab report page for this experiment.

Analysis and Conclusions

1. In your notebook, make a table for each solvent system showing the distance traveled by the solvent front, the distance traveled by each dye, and the R_f value for that dye in that particular solvent system.

2. As best you can, determine the R_f value for each of the dyes in the mixture in each of the solvent mixtures. If you cannot distinguish the distance traveled by one or more of the dyes, say so in your report. For those dye/solvent combinations in which you can determine the R_f values, discuss the degree to which the R_f values in the mixture parallel those for the individual dye spots.

    Would it be possible to use only the R_f values to identify which dye is which in the mixture? Explain.

3. Which solvent mixture gave the *most complete* resolution of the three dyes? Which solvent mixture gave the *poorest* resolution? Which moved up the slide most rapidly? Most slowly?

4. Why is it important to keep the spots applied to TLC slides for chromatography as *small* as possible?

5. Why is it necessary to keep the beaker used for chromatography tightly covered with plastic wrap while the solvent is rising through the TLC slide?

6. TLC slides are most commonly coated with *alumina* or with *silica gel*. Use an outside reference, such as a handbook of chemistry or online source, to find out the composition of each of these materials.

7. In preparing a TLC slide for chromatography, a baseline is drawn *in pencil* for positioning the spots. Why is ink never used for drawing the baseline?

Experiment 15

Heat of Fusion and Freezing Point Depression

Objective

To determine the molar heat of fusion and the molal freezing point depression constant for lauric acid (dodecanoic acid)

Concepts

Heat of fusion, cooling curves, colligative properties, freezing point depression

Introduction

In this experiment you will determine two properties of the same compound, lauric acid, formally known as dodecanoic acid. In Part A, you will determine its *molar enthalpy of fusion*, the amount of heat transferred out of a solid as it melts at its normal melting point. Commonly called the molar heat of fusion, it is represented as ΔH_{fusion}. This is easily done by calorimetry. A tube of molten (melted) lauric acid is placed in a calorimeter just as it reaches its freezing temperature; then when the entire sample has solidified, the tube is removed from the calorimeter. Assuming no heat is lost to the surrounding air, the heat absorbed by the water in the calorimeter must be the same as the heat that flowed out of the solidifying lauric acid. The only tricky part is that you must record two sets of temperatures, one set for the lauric acid in the tube and another for the water in the calorimeter.

Part B illustrates one method for the determination of the molar mass of a pure substance: *freezing point depression*. Because it depends only on the number of solute particles present, but not on their identity, freezing point depression is one of a group of properties known as *colligative properties*. The extent to which the freezing point of a pure substance is lowered (depressed) by the presence of a solute is given by the relation:

$$\Delta T_f = K_f \times m \qquad (15\text{-}1)$$

where ΔT_f is the change in the freezing temperature, m is the molal concentration of the solute, and K_f is a property unique to each solvent, known as the *molal freezing point depression constant*. In this case, lauric acid will be the solvent and benzoic acid will be the solute that depresses the freezing point of the lauric acid. Your goal is to determine K_f for lauric acid.

Recall that molality is defined as the number of moles of solute per kilogram of solvent, or mol/Kg. The change in freezing point is generally measured in degrees Celsius (°C). Rearranging equation 15-1 to solve for K_f gives:

$$K_f = \Delta T_f \div m \qquad (15\text{-}2)$$

and it becomes apparent that the units of K_f are °C/m, degrees Celsius per unit molality. The molal freezing point depression constant for camphor is 37.7 °C/m. This means that one mole of a substance dissolved in 1000 g of camphor will depress the melting point of the camphor by 37.7°C below its normal value of 178.8 °C. The same experiment done with cyclohexane in place of the camphor gives a depression of only 20.0°C, so K_f for cyclohexane is 20.0 °C/m.

You will determine the freezing point of a pure sample of lauric acid, then you will repeat the freezing point determination using a sample of lauric acid to which a known mass of benzoic acid has been added. Your goal is to determine experimentally the value of K_f for lauric acid. Lauric acid is commonly found in soaps and detergents, so you will notice a "soapy" odor. There is minimal health risk. The molecular formulas and abbreviated structural formulas for lauric acid and benzoic acid are given below.

Lauric acid: $C_{12}H_{24}O_2$ $CH_3(CH_2)_{10}COOH$

Benzoic acid: $C_7H_6O_2$ C_6H_5COOH

Prelaboratory Assignment

1. Read the entire experiment before you begin.

2. Prepare separate data tables for Part A and Part B.

Prelaboratory Questions

1. In the Introduction, K_f is described as having the units °C/m (degrees Celsius per unit molality). The AP Chemistry test expresses the units of K_f as K kg mol^{-1}, that is Kelvins times kilograms, times the reciprocal of moles. Show that (K kg mol^{-1}) is equivalent to °C/m.

2. In a typical experiment, a 50.0-mg sample of an unknown solid lowered the freezing point of a 1.00-g sample of camphor by 7.8°C. What is the molecular weight of the unknown solid? K_f for camphor is 37.7 °C/m, or 37.7 K kg mol-1.

3. At the start of Part B, you are directed to weigh out a mass of benzoic acid that is 1/8 the mass of the lauric acid in your tube. Assume your tube contains 9.857 g of lauric acid.

   a. What mass of benzoic acid do you need?

   b. How many moles of benzoic acid is this?

   c. What is the molality of the resulting lauric acid-benzoic acid solution?

Safety Precautions

1. Chemical splash-protective eyewear must be worn at all times in the laboratory.

2. Benzoic acid is a mild irritant. In particular, because it is a very light solid and easily blown about, it may cause some nasal irritation. Keep your hands away from your face as much as possible. Wash your hands thoroughly with soap and water after handling benzoic acid and before leaving the laboratory.

3. Like all organic materials, lauric acid and benzoic acid are highly combustible. Keep them away from open flames. Handle the hot test tube with care.

Materials

Part A

Apparatus   *Reagents*

test tube, 18 x 150 mm, or similar   lauric acid

beakers, 250 mL (2)   water

digital thermometers (2)

hot plate or other means of heating water

coffee-cup calorimeter (2 expanded polystyrene cups, supported by a 250-mL beaker)

Notes: One of the beakers is to be used as the base for the calorimeter; the other is for heating water. For best results, at least one of the thermometers should be long enough to reach the bottom of the test tube (stem length $\geq$ 15 cm).

Part B

Apparatus

digital thermometer, 11 in. or similar
test tube, 18 x 150 mm or similar
250 mL beaker (for heating water)

Reagents

lauric acid
benzoic acid

Procedure

Part A

Overview: Both partners must take an active role if the experiment is to be successfully completed. During the time that the tube of lauric acid is in the calorimeter, one will be responsible for observing the temperature of the lauric acid at 30-second intervals. The other will monitor the temperature of the calorimeter water with the same frequency.

1. Weigh a clean, dry 25 x 150 mm test tube (or similar) to ±1 mg. Fill it about 2/3 of the way with lauric acid, wipe any excess off the outside of the tube, and weigh the tube and contents to ±1 mg. The mass of lauric acid will be about 10 g.

    Note: You will need some sort of support for placing the tube on the balance pan. A plastic drinking cup (6 oz or larger) is tall enough to support the tube without overloading the balance.

2. Lauric acid has a melting point of between 40 °C and 45 °C. Heat some water in one of your 250-mL beakers until it is steaming; this begins at about 50 °C, so once you see that, you know the water is hot enough to melt the lauric acid. You do not need to check the temperature of the water in the heating bath. Doing so may adversely affect your results, in fact. When the water is warm enough to begin to melt the lauric acid, insert a digital thermometer into the tube, then use the thermometer to *gently* stir the solid as it melts; this will speed the melting process.

3. Put about 100 mL (accurately measured) of room-temperature water in the calorimeter. A 6-oz cup made of expanded-polystyrene has a maximum capacity near 200. mL, but the tube will displace some water. You will use the second digital thermometer to monitor the temperature of the calorimeter water (only!). You will need to know by how much the temperature of the calorimeter water increases as the lauric acid turns from liquid to solid.

4. Once the solid acid is nearly melted, especially if the thermometer in the test tube rises above 50°C, you can remove the tube of lauric acid from the heating bath. The residual heat in the tube will complete the melting process. Be certain to turn off the hot plate when heating is done.

    Note: If the temperature of the melted lauric acid is much over 50 °C, let it cool a bit before you place the tube in the calorimeter.

5. When the temperature of the lauric acid drops below 45 °C **or** when you begin to see crystals forming at the surface of the liquid in the tube, place the tube of lauric acid into the calorimeter water. Note and record the temperature readings on both thermometers at the instant crystals appear, then every 30 seconds thereafter, until freezing is complete (see step 6). It is normal for crystallization to begin almost at once when the tube is placed into the calorimeter. Use the digital thermometer to gently stir the contents of the tube until the lauric acid has solidified to the point that the thermometer no longer moves easily. To ensure that the calorimeter water is warmed uniformly, try to move the tube around slowly in the calorimeter.

6. The temperature in the test tube should level at about 43–44 °C (this varies from one thermometer to another, so your results may differ). When you see that the temperature of the lauric acid has dropped below its leveling point, remove the tube from the calorimeter, noting and recording the temperature of the water in the calorimeter. See the section for Disposal for Part A.

Part B
Overview: This portion of the experiment follows the same general procedure as Part A, but with two important differences. First, benzoic acid will be added as a solute. Second, you will not need to record the water temperature in the calorimeter. You will use the same tube of lauric acid *and the same digital thermometer* as was used for Part A. If you have not already done so, carefully remove the thermometer from the lauric acid, wipe off the probe with a dry paper towel, then with a cloth that has been soaked in ethanol. The calorimeter from Part A now serves only as a cooling bath.

7. Weigh the tube and remaining lauric acid. If the total mass of lauric acid has dropped below 8 g, add more lauric acid as needed, then reweigh tube and contents.

8. Weigh out, as accurately as possible, a mass of benzoic acid that is one-eighth of the mass of lauric acid in your tube. Weigh the benzoic acid onto a weighing boat or a piece of wax paper that has a crease down the middle, to make it easy to pour the solid into your tube.

9. Now slide the benzoic acid carefully and quantitatively into the tube. Replace the thermometer, then re-melt the contents of the tube in the hot water bath. As before, use the thermometer to stir the mixture as it melts. Stirring is even more critical this time around, as you want to be sure that the mixture is indeed homogeneous.

10. Repeat the cooling curve experiment. This time, you will see that instead of a plateau, there will be a continuous gradual slope, such as appears in the following sketch. Try to think of the curve as three connected segments. The first and third are relatively steep, while the middle segment has a more gradual slope. As the solution freezes, the molality of the solution is changing, so there is really no leveling point. Instead, it is the start of the middle segment that is taken as the (initial) freezing point of the solution.

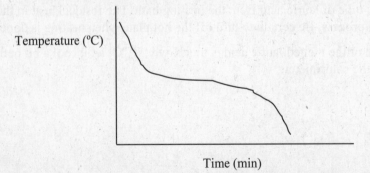

Temperature (°C)

Time (min)

Figure 15–1. A typical cooling curve for a mixture.

Disposal

Part A

1. The tube of lauric acid is to be used again in Part B, but you are finished with the calorimeter and the thermometer that was used for it. Your teacher will tell you what is to be done with the polystyrene cups. If you are planning to complete both parts of the experiment in the same laboratory period, begin re-warming the heating bath. If not, it, too, can be emptied and put away.

Part B

2. There is no easy way to remove the lauric acid-benzoic acid from the tube, so you teacher may elect to have you discard it. If you are to try to clean the tube, melt the acid mixture as you've done twice previously, then quickly pour the liquefied acid mixture onto several thicknesses of paper towels. The material will quickly solidify and cool, and can be placed in the waste basket.

3. All other equipment is to be cleaned and put away in its proper location. Clean the thermometer by wiping first with a dry paper towel, then with a cloth soaked in ethanol.

Analysis and Conclusions

Part A

Your write-up should include all of your data: masses and the time vs. temperature data for the water in the calorimeter and for lauric acid. All calculations are to be shown in the notebook.

1. Make a graph of time vs. temperature, with the curve for lauric acid in one color and that for the water in the calorimeter in another color. Place marks on the lauric acid curve indicating the freezing range, specifically the temperatures at the start and at the end of the freezing process. The freezing point is determined by the method of intersecting lines, as described for Figure 15-3, in Part B.

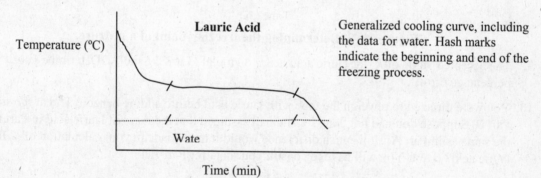

Generalized cooling curve, including the data for water. Hash marks indicate the beginning and end of the freezing process.

Figure 15–2. Expected shape for pure lauric acid.

2. Determine how much heat was transferred to the water as the lauric changed from liquid to solid. This must be the heat released by the lauric acid as it underwent the change of phase. (Hint: Recall $q = s \times m \times \Delta T$.)

3. Use the sample mass and molar mass of lauric acid to determine how many moles of the acid are in the tube.

4. Use the results of questions 2 and 3 to determine the molar heat of fusion, ΔH_{fusion}, of lauric acid in kJ/mol $C_{12}H_{24}O_2$.

Part B

5. Plotting temperature (T, in °C) as a function of time (t, in minutes) will produce a curve similar in shape to the sketch below. To determine the freezing point of the mixture, make two best-fit straight lines (dotted lines in the sketch), then use the temperature at which they intersect as the freezing point. The freezing point of the mixture will be lower than the one you got for pure lauric acid. Figure 15-3, on the next page illustrates this.

6. From the mass and molar mass of benzoic acid, C_6H_5COOH, determine how many moles of benzoic acid were present in solution in your tube.

7. Convert the mass of lauric acid in your tube to kg, then determine the molality of your benzoic acid-lauric acid mixture.

8. Use Equation 15-2, given in the Introduction to determine your experimental value of K_f for lauric acid.

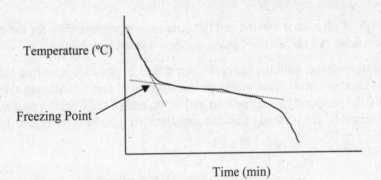

Figure 15–3. Determining the freezing point of a mixture.

9. The accepted value of K_f for lauric acid is 3.9 °C/molal (3.9 K kg mol⁻¹). Determine your percentage error.

10. You were directed to reweigh the tube with lauric acid before adding benzoic acid at the start of Part B. Suppose you had not done so, and had assumed that the mass of lauric acid in Part B was the same as in Part A. How much difference would it have made in your calculation of K_f for lauric acid? (Hint: You will have to consult your data for Part A.)

Experiment 16

Synthesis and Analysis of Aspirin

Objective

To synthesize acetylsalicylic acid (aspirin), then analyze the purity of the product by colorimetric means

Concepts

Organic synthesis, functional groups, recrystallization, colorimetry

Introduction

To a chemist, large organic molecules are most easily thought of in terms of the *functional groups* that make them up. These functional groups are clusters of atoms that are found to occur in the same sequence in many different compounds. Just as simple molecules are viewed as being made up of individual atoms, more complex molecules are often identified by the functional groups that they contain. Some examples appear below. The hydroxyl group is neutral, unlike hydroxide ion, OH⁻. Also shown is the carboxylic acid group. Below these are three ring structures. The first is benzene, which consists of a ring of six carbon atoms, one at each corner of the hexagon, joined together by alternating single and double bonds. Each carbon atom is understood to be bonded to a hydrogen atom. In the middle structure, benzoic acid, one of the hydrogen atoms, has been replaced by a carboxylic acid group, which we can represent as shown on the left, below:

Figure 16-1.
Hydroxyl Group

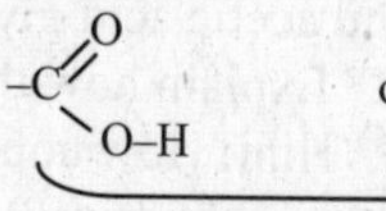

Figure 16-2. The Carboxylic Acid Group

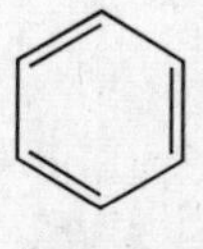

Figure 16-3.
Benzene

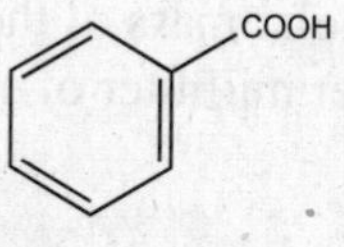

Figure 16-4.
Benzoic Acid

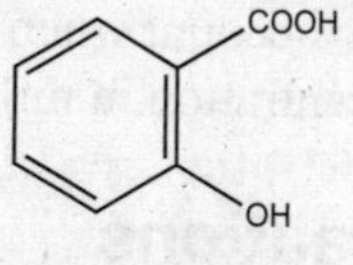

Figure 16-5.
Salicylic Acid

The third structure represents one of the reagents that you will use in this experiment, salicylic acid (its formal name is 2-hydroxybenzoic acid). Now, in addition to the carboxylic acid group, there is a hydroxyl group on the adjacent carbon atom. Below you will see the reaction that you will carry out in the first part of the experiment. The reactants, salicylic acid and acetic anhydride, will be combined to produce acetylsalicylic acid (aspirin) and acetic acid.

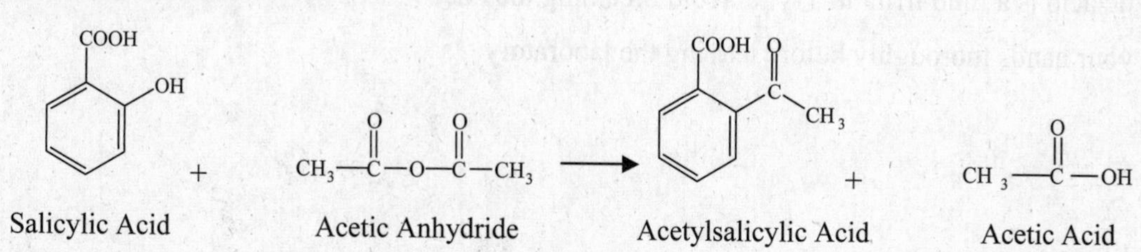

Salicylic Acid   Acetic Anhydride   Acetylsalicylic Acid   Acetic Acid

In the second part of the experiment, you will test the purity of your aspirin by visual colorimetric analysis. Because all of the other reactants and products involved in Part A are either liquids or are very soluble in water, the only species present in your dried product are assumed to be aspirin and any remaining unreacted salicylic acid.

Analysis of the purity of your product takes advantage of the fact that free salicylic acid forms a complex ion with iron(III) ion, Fe^{3+}, that has a distinctive violet color. Because the aqueous metal ion by itself has a faint yellow color, and because the two organic compounds give colorless solutions (as, of course, does chloride ion), unreacted salicylic acid is readily detected by presence of the violet color. In fact, since moist air can cause aspirin to decompose over time into salicylic acid and acetic acid, a quick-and-dirty test you can use to test aspirin that has passed its label expiration date is to shake it with a solution of iron(III) ion, such as $FeCl_3(aq)$. A quantitative determination of the amount of unreacted salicylic acid can be made by measuring the intensity of the violet color, either visually or by use of a spectrophotometer. In either case, a set of standards is prepared by making a series of dilutions of a salicylic acid solution of known concentration, then each dilution is reacted with iron(III) ion. The color intensity varies with the salicylic acid concentration. A solution of the product from Part A is tested with iron(III) and the intensity of its color is compared with the range of intensities of the standards.

Prelaboratory Assignment

1. Read the entire experiment before you begin.

2. In your notebook, prepare data tables for parts A and B of the procedure.

Prelaboratory Questions

1. Examine the structures of acetic anhydride and acetic acid given in the introduction. Look up the meaning of the term "anhydride." Explain how the definition of anhydride is appropriate in the case of acetic anhydride. (Hint: How could two molecules of acetic acid be combined to form one molecule of acetic anhydride?)

2. Give directions for preparing 100.0 mL of 0.100 M iron(III) chloride solution from solid reagent iron(III) chloride hexahydrate, $FeCl_3 \cdot 6H_2O$. (Remember to take the waters of hydration into account when calculating the molar mass of the solute.) Express the solution concentration in milligrams of Fe^{3+} per milliliter of solution (mg Fe^{3+}/mL).

Safety Precautions

1. Chemical splash-protective eyewear must be worn at all times in the laboratory.

2. Acetic anhydride has a very strong and sharp odor. Dispense it in the fume hood.

3. While handling the acetic anhydride, gloves are recommended.

4. Phosphoric acid is corrosive to skin and clothing. Handle it with care and clean up all spills immediately, using large amounts of water.

5. Salicylic acid is a mild irritant. Try to avoid breathing the dust.

6. Wash your hands thoroughly before leaving the laboratory.

Materials

Apparatus

milligram balance

13 x 100 mm test tube with cork

small stirring rod or capillary tube

steam bath or hot water bath

25-mL volumetric flask

96-well test plate (flat-bottom preferably)

Reagents

salicylic acid

acetic anhydride

concentrated phosphoric acid

distilled water

standard salicylic acid solution

50% aqueous ethanol (solvent for Part B)

iron(III) chloride test solution

Procedure

Part A: Synthesis of Aspirin

1. Weigh out (±1 mg) a sample of salicylic acid between 75 and 100 mg in a small test tube.

2. **This step should be done under the hood.** Taking care to keep it off your skin, add 20 drops of acetic anhydride and 3–5 drops of concentrated (85%) phosphoric acid to the salicylic acid in your test tube. Return to your work area, and continue the procedure.

3. Holding the tube in a small clamp, heat the mixture on a steam bath or in a beaker of very hot water (~90°C; the water is simmering, but not fully boiling) for five minutes to complete the reaction.

4. Cautiously add 10 drops of water, cork the tube, and shake well—trying not to get the cork wet, as it will absorb material. Add 10 more drops of water and then cool the tube in an ice bath. Crystals should begin to form as the mixture cools; if they do not, try scratching the inside of the tube with a glass stirring rod. Use a plastic microtip pipet or Pasteur pipet to remove as much liquid as possible from your crystalline product. Do this by lightly squeezing the air from a pipette as you push it through the crystals to the bottom of the tube. Gently release the bulb and slowly pull the liquid into the pipette. If you have good contact between the pipette tip and the bottom of the tube, filtration occurs, allowing you to extract liquid but not solid product.

5. To recrystallize the aspirin, add just enough water to barely cover the crystals, then heat the tube on a steam bath or a hot water bath as before. Heating should bring the sample into solution. Do not waste time during this procedure; prolonged heating of aspirin with water will decompose it.

   Add more water only if it is needed; by no means should the total exceed about 0.5 mL, which is just enough to fill the curved part at the bottom of the tube.

   Allow the tube to cool spontaneously to room temperature and then cool it in an ice bath. Once again, remove as much water as possible from the crystals and scrape the crystals onto a piece of filter paper and squeeze them between sheets of filter paper to remove the water. Place the filter paper containing your product in a safe place where it can air-dry until the following laboratory period.

   Once the product is dry, determine its mass and, if so instructed, its melting point. Examine the crystalline product with a hand lens, if available, comparing the crystal shape of the product to that of the salicylic acid starting material.

Part B: Analysis of the Product

Both aspirin and salicylic acid have limited water solubility. For that reason, a co-solvent system is needed for the test. A solution containing approximately 100 mg of salicylic acid in 100 ml of a 50:50 mixture of ethanol and water has been prepared for you; the precise concentration is given on the container label. Record that concentration for use in the calculations to be done later. There is additional prepared solvent mixture for use in dissolving your solid product for analysis.

6. Using a 25-mL volumetric flask, prepare a solution of your product from Part A by dissolving about 25 mg (± 1 mg) of your dry product in 25.0 ml of 50:50 water/ethanol solvent mixture. Completely dissolve the solid before proceeding.

7. Place one drop of the standard salicylic acid solution in well B-1 of your 96-well plate, two drops in B-2, three in B-3, and so on through B-10. Now starting with well B-9 and working down, add one drop of distilled water to B-9, two drops of water to B-8, three drops to B-7, etc., until all 10 wells contain 10 drops of liquid each (well B-10 contains only salicylic acid solution). Add one drop of standard iron(III) test solution to each of the wells in row B and stir each with a toothpick, preferably plastic, or a glass melting point capillary.

8. Place 10 drops of the solution you prepared from your product in each of the first 10 wells of row A. Add one drop of standard iron(III) test solution to each well of row A; each of the 10 wells in row A contains the same combination of reagents. Determine the relative concentration of salicylic acid in your sample by comparing the color caused by addition of Fe^{3+} to your solution (row A) with the colors obtained with the standards in row B. Comparison is most easily done by holding the test plate a few centimeters above a sheet of white paper in a well-lighted area, then looking straight down through the wells.

9. If your material seems to be intermediate between two of the standards, report it as such. If your product gives a more intense color than the mixture in well A-10, you have converted less of the salicylic acid to aspirin than expected. In this case, make a 1:10 dilution of your product solution and repeat the comparison, with 10 drops of the diluted mixture in each of the first 10 wells of row C. As before, add one drop of the ferric ion test solution to each of the wells C-1 through C-10, and compare with row B, as before.

10. Find an old bottle of aspirin, the older the better. Test it for salicylic acid in the same way. The ferric chloride test is a general test for molecules that contain the phenol group. Sketch the structure of salicylic acid (see the Introduction) and show that it contains the phenol structure.

Phenol

Disposal

There is nothing in this experiment that cannot be safely rinsed down the sink with large amounts of water.

Analysis and Conclusions

1. Calculate the theoretical yield of aspirin, based on the mass of salicylic acid you used in Part A of the procedure. Use this and the mass of your dried product to calculate your percentage yield of crude product.

2. Calculate the concentration of salicylic acid present in each of the 10 wells of row B, using the concentration given for the standard salicylic acid solution. (Hint: This is a dilution problem.)

3. Based on the values you calculated in the previous question and the well that gave you the best color match in Part B, estimate the salicylic acid concentration in the solution made from your product. You know the mass of your dried product used per milliliter of the solution that you made, and you have just determined what part of that is unconverted salicylic acid, so the rest must be aspirin. This allows you to calculate the concentration of aspirin (in mg/mL). The relative purity of your aspirin product from Part A is simply the mass ratio of aspirin present per milliliter to product used per milliliter. Multiplication by 100 converts this relative purity to a percent purity value.

$$\text{Relative Purity} = \frac{[\text{aspirin}]}{[\text{crude product}]} \, x100\%$$

4. Calculate your actual percentage yield in the aspirin synthesis by combining the figures for the yield of crude product with the percentage purity.

5. Bottles of aspirin are often dated and have a "use by" date. When you open an old bottle of aspirin it often smells like vinegar. Account for this observation.

Suggestions for Further Investigation

If your teacher directs you to do so, use a spectrophotometer to provide a more precise value of the color comparison. Compare the two methods; how much difference is there in the two results?

Experiment 17

The Partition Coefficient of an Organic Acid

Objective

To determine how an organic acid will distribute itself between water and a nonpolar solvent

Concepts

Effect of solvent polarity on solubility, acid-base titrations

Introduction

Water and cyclohexane are not *miscible*. After being shaken together the two will separate to give two layers with the cyclohexane on top. Some organic molecules will dissolve in both cyclohexane and water. When such a molecule, the *solute*, is dissolved in either solvent and the two layers are shaken together the solute will distribute itself between the two solvents. The purpose of this experiment is to measure quantitatively the *partition coefficient*, which is a measure of the solubilities of the solute in the two solvents.

Inorganic ionic compounds are usually water soluble, but insoluble in nonpolar solvents. Conversely nonpolar organic compounds are not soluble in polar solvents such as water. Some weakly ionic compounds, such as organic acids, are somewhat soluble in both nonpolar and polar solvents.

Nonpolar cyclohexane, C_6H_{12}, and the polar liquid water are not miscible (they do not dissolve in each other); but propanoic acid[1], CH_3CH_2COOH, will dissolve in both. The object of this experiment is to measure how propanoic acid partitions itself between the two immiscible solvent layers and to study the technique of extraction.

If cyclohexane and water are placed in a test tube they will form two layers, with the cyclohexane on top. If propanoic acid is then added to the tube and the mixture is shaken, it will be found, after the layers separate, that some of the acid is in the cyclohexane and some is in the water. The ratio of the concentration in cyclohexane to that in water is a constant, k, called the *partition coefficient*:

$$k = \frac{\text{concentration of acid in upper layer (cyclohexane)}}{\text{concentration of acid in lower layer (water)}}$$

If the top (organic) layer is carefully removed and a fresh portion of cyclohexane is added and the mixture shaken once more, the acetic acid that was in the water layer should again partition itself between the two layers. In this way the acetic acid can be *extracted* from the water. We will try to predict how much acid is extracted each time knowing what the partition coefficient is, and then check this prediction by experiment.

The amount of propanoic acid remaining in the water layer will be determined by titration with sodium hydroxide solution according to the following equation:

$$CH_3CH_2COOH(aq) + NaOH(aq) \rightarrow CH_3CH_2COONa(aq) + H_2O(l)$$

It is difficult to measure microscale quantities of sodium hydroxide solution to 0.001 mL, but it is easy to weigh the solution to 0.001g. In this experiment the solution will be weighed before and after the titration to determine the quantity needed to neutralize the acetic acid.

In the second part of the experiment, because it is not easy to separate layers quantitatively, we will measure the extraction reagents volumetrically, a more rapid process than weighing them.

---

[1] Also called propionic acid.

A solution of propanoic acid is standardized by titration with standard sodium hydroxide. Then the propanoic acid solution is extracted with an equal mass of cyclohexane, after which the amount of acid remaining in the aqueous layer is again determined by titration. Knowing how much acid was extracted allows calculation of the distribution coefficient, the ratio of the amount of acid in cyclohexane to that in the water. Both the standardization of the acid and determination of the partition coefficient will be carried out three times.

Once the partition coefficient has been determined, it should be possible to predict the effect of multiple extractions. The effectiveness of such a prediction will be tested by experiment. This part will be done in a single trial.

Safety Precautions

1. Chemical splash-protective eyewear must be worn at all times in the laboratory.

2. Handle sodium hydroxide solution with care. Wipe up spills with a damp sponge.

3. Cyclohexane, like most organic liquids, is quite flammable. Be sure there are no flames present when working with cyclohexane.

4. After each extraction, remove the stopper from the tube cautiously. Cyclohexane is volatile, and may splash out of the tube.

Prelaboratory Assignment

1. Read the entire experiment before you begin.

2. Reproduce the following data tables in your notebook. Note that these are in small print and spaced too closely together to be used directly. As you prepare your tables, be sure to leave room for calculations anywhere that you see (Show calculation).

1. Standardization of Acetic Acid Solution	1	2	3
Initial mass of pipet containing propanoic acid solution			
Final mass of pipet containing propanoic acid solution			
Mass of propanoic acid solution			
Initial mass of pipet containing sodium hydroxide solution			
Final mass of pipet containing sodium hydroxide solution			
Mass of sodium hydroxide solution			
Concentration of sodium hydroxide in mol/g of solution (On label of container)			
Concentration of propanoic acid solution in mol/g of water (Show calculation)			

2. Extractions with Cyclohexane			
a. Determination of the partition coefficient	1	2	3
Mass of water layer after extraction			
Initial mass of pipet containing sodium hydroxide solution			
Final mass of pipet containing sodium hydroxide solution			
Mass of sodium hydroxide solution			
Concentration (mol/g) of propanoic acid in water layer after extraction (Show calculation)			
Concentration (mol/g) of propanoic acid in cyclohexane layer (Show calculation)			
Partition coefficient, k (Show calculation)			
Average value for partition coefficient, k			

b. Extraction with three portions of cyclohexane

Predicted concentration of propanoic acid in aqueous layer
after three extractions with cyclohexane _____

Mass of aqueous layer after three extraction _____

Initial mass of pipet containing sodium hydroxide solution _____

Final mass of pipet containing sodium hydroxide solution _____

Mass of sodium hydroxide solution _____

Concentration of propanoic acid in water layer after
three extractions (Show calculation) _____

Prelaboratory Questions

1. You wish to prepare 100. mL of 1.00 M propanoic acid solution.

   a. What volume of pure, 13.4 M propanoic acid will you need? Assuming that volume is conserved in this process, what volume of water will be needed?

   b. The density of pure propanoic acid is 0.993 g mL^{-1}; that of distilled water is 1.00 g/mL. What is the total mass of the solution?

   c. Calculate the concentration of the solution in moles of propanoic acid per gram of solution.

2. Suppose the extraction of 1.00 mL of an unknown organic acid was carried out in two different ways. In case (a), the acid is extracted once, using 3 mL of cyclohexane. In a separate experiment, a single 1.0-mL sample of the acid is extracted with three successive 1-mL portions of cyclohexane. Calculate the amounts of acid that would be extracted in each case; assume $k = 2.0$ for this acid and that the original acid solution contains 10. mmol of acid.

   Suggestion: For each extraction, let x equal the number of mmol extracted in the cyclohexane layer. In case (a), the concentration in the cyclohexane layer is x mmol/mL and that in the water layer is $(10.-x)$ mmol/mL; the ratio of these quantities is equal to the distribution coefficient, k.

Materials

Apparatus

10 x 100 mm culture tubes
corks or stoppers for tubes
Beral-type pipets
Erlenmeyer flasks, 10-mL

Reagents

propanoic acid solution, (74 g/Kg water)
standard sodium hydroxide solution (40 g/kg water)
phenolphthalein
cyclohexane

Procedure

Part A: Standardization of Propanoic Acid Solution

The concentration of propanoic acid, in mol/g of solution, is determined by titration with sodium hydroxide solution of known concentration.

1. Fill labeled microtip pipets with solutions of:
   a) Propanoic acid
   b) Standard sodium hydroxide solution (record the concentration of sodium hydroxide in moles of NaOH per gram of solution, mol NaOH/g)
   c) Phenolphthalein indicator solution

2. Weigh the pipets containing the acid and base. Place approximately 1 mL of the propanoic acid solution in a 10 mL Erlenmeyer flask. This is about 1/3 the capacity of a pipet. Reweigh the pipet and remaining acid. Add one drop of indicator to the flask and mix well by swirling.

3. Weigh the sodium hydroxide pipet and then titrate the acid solution by adding sodium hydroxide dropwise, swirling the flask after every few drops. The *endpoint,* or *equivalence point,* of the *titration* will be signaled by the appearance of a pink color that persists throughout the body of the solution for at least 30 seconds. Weigh the pipet containing the remaining sodium hydroxide solution. If the endpoint is overshot, the reaction can be back-titrated by adding more propanoic acid.

4. Repeat the titration at least two more times, then calculate the ratio of mass of base solution to mass of acid solution. If the three ratios do not agree within 1%, continue doing titrations until you have three ratios that are within sufficient agreement. If after six trials you are unable to achieve agreement on three trials, consult your teacher.

Part B: Extractions with Cyclohexane

a. Determination of the partition coefficient

5. Measure 1 mL of propanoic acid solution into a tared (previously weighed) 10 x 100 mm culture tube, weigh the tube and contents and then use a microtip pipet to add an equal mass of cyclohexane. Stopper the tube with a tightly-fitting cork or stopper and shake it vigorously for about 2 min., then allow the layers to separate. It may be difficult to see the interface between the two layers.

6. With a Pasteur or plastic pipet, withdraw most of the lower layer and place it in a tared Erlenmeyer flask. Do not remove any of the top layer material or any of the material at the interface. Weigh the flask plus aqueous layer. Titrate the propanoic acid in the flask with standard sodium hydroxide to equivalence, as before. Repeat this process at least twice more, starting with a fresh sample of propanoic acid each time.

As part of your report, you will calculate the concentration of propanoic acid in the aqueous layer in moles of CH_3CH_2COOH/gram of solution based on the results of this titration. The concentration of propanoic acid in the cyclohexane layer can be found by difference. The ratio of the two concentrations (concentration of acid in cyclohexane/concentration of acid in water) is the partition coefficient, k.

b. Extraction with three portions of cyclohexane

Using the value for the partition coefficient just obtained, calculate the expected final concentration of propanoic acid that would remain in the aqueous layer after a 1.0-mL sample of propanoic acid has been extracted with three equal weights of cyclohexane, then carry out the experiment.

7. Mix 1.0 mL (about 1.0 g) of propanoic acid solution and 1.3 mL (1.0 g) of cyclohexane. Stopper the tube, then shake the mixture well. When the layers have separated, use a clean microtip or Pasteur pipette to draw off the lower aqueous layer as completely as possible. Try not to remove any of the organic (top) layer. Transfer the aqueous fraction to another, clean culture tube. In this fashion, extract the same aqueous layer twice more with fresh 1.3-mL portions of cyclohexane.

Following the third extraction, titrate the aqueous layer with standard sodium hydroxide solution to determine the actual concentration of propanoic acid remaining after three successive extractions.

As part of your analysis, you will see how well your prediction matches experimental results.

Disposal

The combined cyclohexane layers should be placed in the organic solvents waste container. The aqueous layers, all of which should be neutral because they have been titrated, can be flushed down the drain.

Analysis and Conclusions

1. Based on your experimental results, is propanoic acid more soluble in water or cyclohexane? Explain the basis for your conclusion and offer an explanation for the result.

2. Would it be possible to extract all of the propanoic acid from an aqueous solution using cyclohexane? Why (or why not)?

3. Would it be possible to extract 90.% of the propanoic acid from an aqueous solution using cyclohexane? If not, why not? If so, suggest a process for carrying out the extraction.

4. What would the concentration of propanoic acid in the water have been if the original aqueous solution of propanoic acid were extracted with one 4.0 mL portion of cyclohexane rather than three times with 1.3-mL portions? (Show calculation)

Experiment 18

Vapor Pressure and the Molar Heat of Vaporization
The Clausius-Clapeyron Equation

Objective

To make a plot of vapor pressure versus temperature and to determine the molar heat of vaporization for water, via the Clapeyron equation

Concepts

Vapor pressure, gas laws, the Clapeyron equation

Introduction

At very low temperatures (temperatures near the freezing point), the rate of evaporation of water (or any liquid) is negligible. As temperature increases, however, so does the rate at which a liquid evaporates, until the pressure due to escaping molecules equals the surrounding atmospheric pressure; this is known as the **boiling point** of the liquid. The pressure exerted in a closed container by an evaporating liquid is known as its **vapor pressure**. It is a function only of the temperature of the system and a characteristic property of the liquid that is evaporating.

As you see in Chapter 10 of your text, a relationship known as the Clausius-Clapeyron equation, or simply the Clapeyron equation, relates the molar heat of vaporization of a liquid to the natural logarithm of the vapor pressure to the temperature (in Kelvins). The equation has the form:

$$\ln(P_{vap}) = -\frac{\Delta H_{vap}}{R}\left(\frac{1}{T_K}\right) + C \qquad (18\text{-}1)$$

For any two points on a plot of the natural log of vapor pressure (ln P_{vap}) as a function of reciprocal absolute temperature (1/T), the equation takes the form:

$$\ln(P_{vap}) = -\frac{\Delta H_{vap}}{R}\left(\frac{1}{T_2} - \frac{1}{T_1}\right) \qquad (18\text{-}2)$$

and the slope of the resulting straight line is equal to $\Delta H/R$, where $R = 8.31 \times 10^{-3}$ kJ mol^{-1}K^{-1}. You will use this relation to determine graphically a value for the vapor pressure of water.

Safety Precautions

1. Chemical splash-protective eyewear must be worn at all times in the laboratory.

2. There are no chemical hazards involved, but handle hot glassware with proper care and exercise caution when working around hot plates.

Materials

Apparatus   ### *Reagents*

10-mL graduated cylinder   water
1-L beaker, preferably tall-form   ice
thermometer (not glass, preferably)
large tray or sink for catching overflow

Prelaboratory Assignment

1. Read the entire experiment before you begin.

2. Prepare a data table for recording the volume of gas in the graduate as a function of temperature. While you may not need them all, it's a good idea to leave space for about a dozen pairs of readings. As part of your Analysis and Conclusions, you will make a larger, more comprehensive Summary Table.

Prelaboratory Questions

1. Write the ideal gas law: (a) in standard form; (b) rearranged to solve for n, in terms of P, V, and T; and (c) rearranged to solve for P, in terms of n, V, and T.

2. At any given temperature, what gas other than the trapped air will be in the inverted graduated cylinder?

3. State Dalton's Law of Partial Pressures and explain how it applies to this experimental procedure.

Procedure

1. Place 7–8 mL of water in a 10-mL graduated cylinder, then invert the graduate in a tall-form one-liter beaker or similar tall, heat-tolerant container of water. (**Note:** The entire graduated cylinder must be under water.) Heat the system on a hot plate or ring-stand to a temperature of about 80° C, with gentle stirring to ensure even heating. **Do not use a glass thermometer to stir.**

2. Remove the beaker and graduate from the heat source, and read the volume of moist air in the cylinder to the nearest 0.1 mL and record your value in a Summary Table. (**Note:** You may have to lift the graduate above the water level in the beaker to make this and later volume readings; that should not materially affect your results as long as you work quickly in taking your measurement.)

3. Place the beaker and graduate in a tray or similar container to catch overflow, then add ice one or two pieces at a time, stirring gently to maintain a uniform temperature throughout the system. Continue the <u>gradual</u> cooling, recording the volume of moist air in the graduated cylinder at about five-degree intervals, down to a temperature of about 40° C. You should have at least seven readings, in order to establish a good graph in the Analysis and Conclusions section. Record these volumes and temperatures in the Summary Table.

4. Once you've reached 40°C (or less), add a handful of ice to the beaker of water and stir gently. If this is not sufficient to cool the water below 5° C, add more ice. When the temperature has fallen below 5°C, record the volume and temperature one last time.

    In carrying out the calculations for this experiment, you will need the ambient barometric pressure. Obtain and record this value before leaving the laboratory.

Disposal

All water used in the experiment may be poured down the sink, but it might be better used to water plants or trees.

Analysis and Conclusions

Part A: The Vapor Pressure of Water

Prepare a Summary Table in your notebook with the headings shown below. Leave enough lines for all of your pairs of data points. The values for observed volume (V_{obs}) and T can be taken directly from your data table, although the temperatures must be converted from Celsius degrees to Kelvins. Instructions for the others follow.

Summary Table Headings

V_{obs} (mL)	V_{corr} (mL)	T (K)	n_{air} (mol)	P_{barom} (mmHg)	P_{air} (mmHg)	P_{vapor} (mmHg)

1. The graduated cylinder was calibrated to be read in an upright position. Because your readings were made with the cylinder inverted, the volume must be corrected by subtracting 0.2 mL from each recorded value. Enter the corrected volumes in the Summary Table under [V_{corr}].

2. Below 5° C the vapor pressure of the water is negligible, so may be disregarded since effectively the only gas in the graduated cylinder is the trapped air. We can further assume that the pressure in the cylinder is equal to the barometric pressure. Use these assumptions and the Ideal Gas Law to calculate the number of moles, **n**, of air in the graduated cylinder at your sub-5°C temperature. This value does not change, so the same value for **n** may be entered in each row of your table. The barometric pressure, too, does not change, so the values for this column will all be the same.

3. Use your volume measurements for each of the other temperatures and the value of **n** obtained in question 2 to calculate the pressure due to air at each of the other temperatures. Answers will be <u>less than</u> the barometric pressure, because at each of these temperatures the graduate contains both air and water vapor.

4. At each of the temperatures, the difference between the calculated pressure (from question 3) and the barometric pressure is the vapor pressure of water at that temperature. For each temperature enter the atmospheric pressure, the pressure due to air, and the vapor pressure of water in the appropriate columns of your table.

5. Plot vapor pressure as a function of temperature. Draw the best smooth-curve fit you can. Your graph should occupy at least half a page in your notebook.

    Compare your results with the accepted values and curve shape, as found in your text or other reference. Discuss your findings.

Part B: The Molar Heat of Vaporization of Water

6. Make a new table showing ln P_{vap} and T^{-1}. Plot the data from the table, placing *ln P* on the vertical axis and T^{-1} on the horizontal axis. Because your reciprocal temperatures are all going to be on the order of 0.003, it is most convenient to convert these values to scientific notation and to label only the coefficients on the x-axis scale. Thus, since temperatures will range from just above 273 K *up to* about 360. K, T^{-1} will range from 3.66×10^{-3} *down to* 2.78×10^{-3}; the axis might be marked off starting at 2.70 and ranging up to 3.70, with the label being: T^{-1} ($\times 10^{3}$), showing that each value on that scale actually carries an exponential value of 10^{-3}.

Draw the best straight-line fit through the points. It is normal for the line to curve a bit at the end; if this happens, ignore the "tail" and go with the best fit for the bulk of your data points.

Determine the slope of your line; it is equal to $-\Delta H_{vap}/R$. Solve for $\Delta H_{vaporization}$, the molar heat of vaporization of water. Look up the accepted value and determine your percentage error.

Experiment 19

Hydrolysis of *t*-Butyl Chloride
A Kinetics Investigation

Objective

To determine the rate law and the specific rate constant for a chemical reaction

Concepts

Reaction kinetics, reaction order, reaction mechanisms

Introduction

One of the goals of chemical kinetics is to determine, as best we can, the sequence of steps that take place in chemical reactions. This sequence of steps is called the *reaction mechanism*. According to collision theory, any single step is unlikely to involve more than two molecules since the possibility of more than two molecules meeting at the same instant and all with the proper spatial orientation is statistically improbable. When a reaction proceeds via a sequence of steps, the rate of the reaction is governed by the slowest of the steps, called the *rate determining step*.

The particular reaction that you will be investigating is the one that occurs between hydroxide ions and a compound known as *tertiary*-butyl chloride, or *t*-butyl chloride for short. The "tertiary" refers to the fact that the central carbon in the molecule is bonded to three other carbon atoms. In Figure 19-1, the central carbon atom is represented by the intersection of the four bonds. The smaller methyl group is understood to be behind the plane of the paper, as shown, too, by the broken like that represents the bond to the central carbon atom. The chloride ion, by contrast, is larger than the other atoms, and its heavy bond shows that it extends out in front of the plane of the paper.

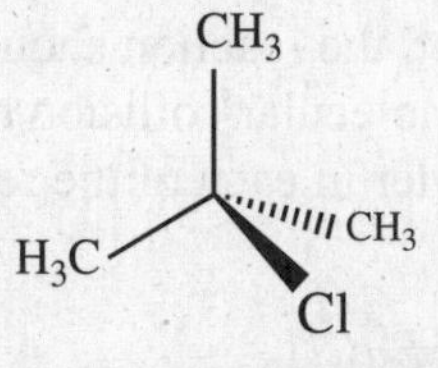

Figure 19-1. *t*-Butyl Chloride

When *t*-butyl chloride is allowed to react with excess hydroxide ions, the chlorine atom is replaced by a hydroxyl group, yielding *t*-butyl alcohol, or *t*-butanol, shown in Figure 19-2.

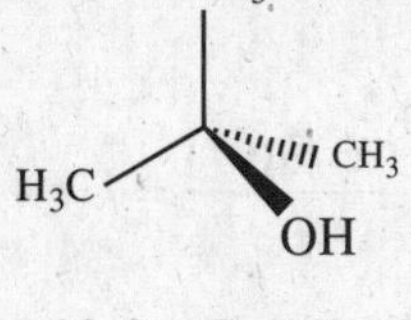

Figure 19-2. *t*-Butyl Alcohol

In molecular form, the reaction equation looks like this:

$$(CH_3)_3CCl + OH^- \rightarrow (CH_3)_3COH + Cl^- \qquad (19\text{-}1)$$

You will consider two possibilities for the mechanism. One is that the reaction proceeds via a collision between a hydroxide ion and the central carbon atom. This bimolecular collision would result in an intermediate structure such as the one shown in Figure 19-3. This structure may be thought of as the activated complex for the reaction.

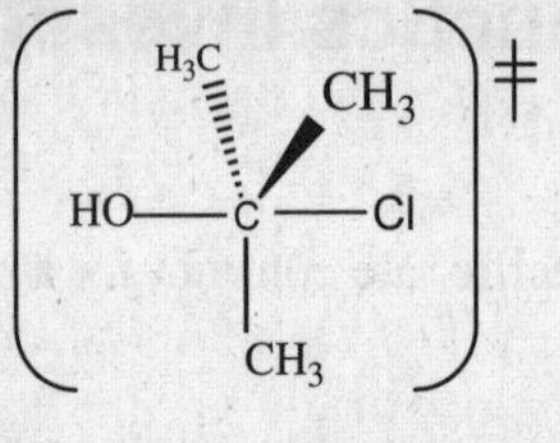

Figure 19-3. Possible Activated Complex for a One-Step Mechanism

This particle could then come apart, with the chlorine atom leaving and the hydroxyl group remaining, giving the product t-butyl alcohol (Figure 19-2). If the reaction proceeds in this fashion, then the reaction rate would be expected to be first order in both hydroxide ion and *t*-butyl chloride, and the expected rate law would be:

$$\text{rate} = k[t\text{-BuCl}][OH^-] \tag{19-2}$$

where [*t*-BuCl] and [OH⁻] represent the molar concentrations of *t*-butyl chloride and hydroxide ion, respectively. This would mean that the reaction was second order overall.

An alternative route to completion would involve two steps. In the first, the *t*-butyl chloride separates into ions, presumably a slow, reversible process. This would be followed by a second, rapid step in which the cation from step 1, called a *carbonium* ion (or *carbocation*), would rapidly add a hydroxide ion, producing the *t*-butyl alcohol.

$$Step\ 1:\ (CH_3)_3CCl \underset{}{\overset{slow}{\rightleftharpoons}} (CH_3)_3C^{\oplus} + Cl^- \tag{19-3}$$

$$Step\ 2:\ (CH_3)_3C^{\oplus} + OH^- \xrightarrow{rapid} (CH_3)_3COH \tag{19-4}$$

Regardless of which mechanism is correct, the reaction should be first order in *t*-butyl chloride. If the first mechanism is correct, in which a bimolecular collision between *t*-butyl chloride and hydroxide ion occurs, the reaction should be first order in each of the reactants, leading to the rate law shown in Equation 19-5.

$$rate = \frac{^2[t-BuCl]}{^2t} = k[t-BuCl][OH^-] \tag{19-5}$$

If the second mechanism is the correct one, the rate should be first order with respect to *t*-butyl chloride concentration but independent of hydroxide ion concentration. In such a case we say the reaction is zero order with respect to hydroxide. The rate law in this case would be that shown in Equation 19-6.

$$rate = \frac{^2[t-BuCl]}{^2t} = k[t-BuCl] \tag{19-6}$$

You will decide which of the two possible mechanisms is more likely by carrying out a series of timed reactions, divided into three parts. The first part will establish that the rate of reaction can be measured with reliable certainty. This will be done by carrying out the reaction three times, using identical quantities of the reactants.

In the second part, the concentration of *t*-butyl chloride is varied, while that of hydroxide ion is held constant. In this way you will confirm that the reaction is, indeed, first order in *t*-butyl chloride. You will make plots of [*t*-BuCl] versus time and ln[*t*-BuCl] versus time. The first is not expected to be linear, as you know, but a linear plot for ln [*t*-BuCl] will confirm that the reaction is first order with respect to the initial concentration of *t*-butyl chloride. The final set of runs will test the dependence of rate on the concentration of hydroxide ion.

In all, there will be seven runs, each of which follows the same pattern: a solution of *t*-butyl chloride in acetone is added to an aqueous solution of sodium hydroxide, to which a small amount of bromthymol blue indicator has been added. To ensure results that are as consistent as possible, each of your trials will have the same total volume and the same proportion of water to acetone.

A color change for the indicator will signal the point at which all of the excess hydroxide ion has been consumed. In the presence of hydroxide, bromthymol blue is blue in color, but it turns yellow when the pH drops below 7. When all of the excess hydroxide has been consumed, the color of the bromthymol blue either will turn from blue to green, showing that the system is no longer alkaline, or it will turn to yellow due to a secondary reaction in which the carbonium ion produced, as shown in Equation *19-4*, reacts with water, producing hydronium ion. See Equation *19-7*.

$$(CH_3)_3C^{\oplus} + 2H_2O \xrightarrow{rapid} (CH_3)_3COH + H_3O^+ \qquad (19\text{-}7)$$

Part A involves a reaction mixture in which there is just enough hydroxide ion to consume 10.% of the *t*-butyl chloride present. This condition was chosen because, as you recall, the rate of a reaction is relatively constant at first, but becomes more gradual as the process continues and the curve of concentration versus time flattens out. In the second and third runs, as the concentration of *t*-butyl chloride is decreased, a greater fraction of the molecules must react in order to bring about the color change of the indicator. This will result in longer times for the color change to take place. See the discussion of the "method of initial rates" in your text.

Once that set of reactions has been completed, you will carry out a final set to see how the rate is affected by changes in the concentration of hydroxide ion as the *t*-butyl chloride concentration is held constant. Using the results of both parts, you will be able to write the rate law for the reaction and to calculate a value for the specific rate constant, *k*.

Prelaboratory Assignment

1. Read the entire experiment before coming to the laboratory.

2. Prepare a data table in your notebook in which you will record the times for each reaction trial. Note that there are five combinations to be tested, with the first being carried out three times, to establish consistency of results. Consult the Procedure for the way to identify the various runs.

Prelaboratory Questions

1. Determine the mass and volume of *t*-butyl chloride needed to make 250. mL of a 0.10 *M* solution, with acetone as the solvent. The density of *t*-butyl chloride is 0.842 g/mL.

2. Show that the two steps of the mechanism described by equations *19-3* and *19-4* give the same overall stoichiometry as is indicated by Equation *19-1*.

3. Calculate the initial concentrations (at the instant of mixing) of *t*-butyl chloride and hydroxide ion in each of the four combinations. Show that, for Run 1, the initial concentrations are in a 1:10 ratio. What happens to the value of this ratio as you do the ensuing runs? What would you expect to happen to the time needed to consume 10.% of the *t*-butyl chloride? Explain.

4. Determine the percents by volume of water and acetone in each reaction mixture. Suggest an explanation for the fact that it is essential to keep this proportion constant throughout all of the trials. (Hint: consider the first step of the two-step mechanism.)

Safety Precautions

1. Chemical splash-protective eyewear must be worn at all times in the laboratory.

2. The organic compounds used in this experiment are all flammable and moderately toxic by ingestion.

3. Sodium hydroxide is corrosive to skin and clothing. Wipe up all spills with large amounts of water.

Materials

Apparatus

Erlenmeyer flasks, 30–50 mL (14, if possible)
graduated cylinder, 25 mL
pipet, 1.0 x 0.01 mL, glass, not plastic
pipet, 10 x 0.1 mL, glass, not plastic
pipet, 5.0 x 0.1 mL, glass, not plastic
stopwatch

Reagents

t-butyl chloride solution, 0.10 *M* in acetone
sodium hydroxide, NaOH(aq), 0.10 *M*
acetone, $C_3H_6O(l)$
bromthymol blue indicator, 0.04%(aq)

Procedure

1. Determine in advance which partner will do the timing. It is critical that timing begins at the instant of first mixing and ends when the color of the reaction mixture flashes to yellow. All of your trials will follow the same three-step procedure:

    1) Pour the contents of Flask 1 into Flask 2 as you start timing.

    2) Swirl briefly (1–2 s).

    3) Pour back into Flask 1; time to yellow.

2. The first combination (Runs 1a, 1b, and 1c) is to be done three times, to get consistent results. If necessary, carry out additional trials until you have three that show good agreement, shown by times that span 1.0 second or less.

    If it is necessary for you to clean your flasks from time to time, be sure that you dry the flasks, inside and out, to prevent dilution. Follow the instructions given in the Disposal section, below. If you have access to a source of compressed air, give the flasks a final rinse with acetone, then dry them with an air stream.

3. The combinations are given below; note that in Part B, as the volume of *t*-butyl chloride in Flask 1 decreases, the decrease is compensated for by addition of an equal volume of acetone, so that the total volume and solvent composition is always the same. Likewise, in Part C, as the volume of 0.10 *M* NaOH is varied, the volume of distilled water (d. H_2O) is adjusted to maintain a total volume of 14.00 mL.

    Do not leave the *t*-butyl chloride standing in an open container for longer than necessary. Both it and the acetone in which it is dissolved are quite volatile, and evaporation will result in changing concentrations.

4. Due to the volatility of the organic solution, it is recommended that you prepare the samples for each part, then carry out those runs only. The care with which you prepare each solution and the accuracy of your measurements will be the determining factors in your successful completion of the experiment.

5. If a significant length of time elapses between Part A and Part C, it might be a good idea to add another trial that duplicates the volumes of reagents used in Part A. A single run will suffice.

Combinations To Be Tested

Part A: Establishing a consistent baseline: All combinations are the same.

Run 1a: **Flask 1:**   6.0 mL 0.10 M *t*-butyl chloride
              Flask 2:   0.60 mL 0.10 M NaOH + 13.40 mL d. H_2O + bromthymol blue

Run 1b: **Flask 1:**   6.0 mL 0.10 M *t*-butyl chloride
              Flask 2:   0.60 mL 0.10 M NaOH + 13.40 mL d. H_2O + bromthymol blue

Run 1c: **Flask 1:**   6.0 mL 0.10 M *t*-butyl chloride
              Flask 2:   0.60 mL 0.10 M NaOH + 13.40 mL d. H_2O + bromthymol blue

Part B: Determining reaction order with respect to [t-BuCl]: [*t*-BuCl] is varied while [OH⁻] is held constant.

Run 2:   **Flask 1:**   5.0 mL 0.10 M *t*-butyl chloride + 1.0 mL acetone
              Flask 2:   0.60 mL 0.10 M NaOH + 13.40 mL d. H_2O + bromthymol blue

Run 3:   **Flask 1:**   4.0 mL 0.10 M *t*-butyl chloride + 2.0 mL acetone
              Flask 2:   0.60 mL 0.10 M NaOH + 13.40 mL d. H_2O + bromthymol blue

Part C: Determining reaction order with respect to [OH⁻]: [*t*-BuCl] is held constant while [OH⁻] is varied.

Run 4:   **Flask 1:**   6.0 mL 0.10 M *t*-butyl chloride
              Flask 2:   1.0 mL 0.10 M NaOH + 13.00 mL d. H_2O + bromthymol blue

Run 5:   **Flask 1:**   6.0 mL 0.10 M *t*-butyl chloride
              Flask 2:   0.40 mL 0.10 M NaOH + 13.60 mL d. H2O + bromthymol blue

Disposal

1. Empty the contents of reaction vessels into the container labeled "Volatile Organic Waste."

2. Wash the flasks with soap and water, followed by a distilled-water rinse and an acetone rinse. If the flasks are to be used again immediately, dry each one, inside and out, to prevent dilution of the reagents in the next trial. If you have access to a source of compressed air, it will speed the drying process.

Analysis and Conclusions

Part A

1. Average the times that you recorded for the three runs. Calculate the percentage deviation for the three trials.

Part B

2. Make a plot of initial concentration of *t*-butyl chloride versus time needed to reach completion. Use the concentrations that you calculated in prelaboratory question 3 and the average time for each combination. Draw the best smooth curve you can through the data points; they will not form a straight line. This plot and the one that follows should each occupy most of a sheet of the graph paper, which is available at the end of this manual.

3. Make a plot of the natural log of the initial *t*-butyl chloride concentration versus time, $\ln[t\text{-BuCl}]_0$ versus time, again using the data from prelaboratory question 3 and the average time for each combination. Draw the best-fit straight line through your three data points and calculate its slope, if it appears linear. If the points do not appear to form a straight line, make the best smooth curve you can. Calculate the slope of this line.

   Attach this plot and the one from question 2 to your report when you hand it in.

Part C

4. You found that instead of increasing the rate of reaction, using a higher concentration of NaOH resulted a longer time for reaction rather than a shorter time, as would be expected if the rate was first order with respect to hydroxide ion. Likewise, decreasing the concentration of hydroxide ion led to a shorter time for reaction. At first glance, this counter-intuitive result may seem confusing, but the seeming anomaly actually supports the two-step mechanism shown in Equations *19-3* and *19-4*.

   In Part A you found that the time needed to generate enough of the carbonium ion, $(CH_3)_3C^{\oplus}$, was quite consistent. Presumably the same was true—the rate of formation of the carbonium ion is constant—for the two trials in Part C. Use this assumption to explain why the time needed for the color change in runs 4 and 5 varies as it does.

5. Based on your results in this experiment, does the reaction appear to be first or second order overall? Which of the two proposed mechanisms best fits the system? Explain.

6. Recalling that the slope of the best-fit line that you drew in response to question 3, above, is equal to $-k$, where k is the specific rate constant for the reaction, give the value of the specific rate constant. Be sure to include the units.

7. Write the rate law for the reaction between *t*-butyl chloride and hydroxide ion.

8. The reaction is, in fact, first order in *t*-butyl chloride and zero-order in hydroxide, and the two-step mechanism described in the Introduction is the accepted one for the system.

   a. How did the color change of the indicator support this mechanism?

   b. How would you expect the rate of reaction to be affected if the proportion of water to acetone were changed? Be specific and cite the reasons for your prediction.

Experiment 20

Investigating Acid-Base Equilibria

Objective

To observe the pH and solubility behavior of selected chemical systems

Concepts

Acids and bases, strong and weak electrolytes, acidic and basic hydrolysis

Introduction

According to the Arrhenius model, acids increase the hydrogen ion concentration, $[H^+]$, of water, while bases increase the concentration of hydroxide ion, $[OH^-]$. Thus, acids dissociate or ionize in water according to:

$$HX(aq) \rightarrow H^+(aq) + X^-(aq) \qquad (20\text{-}1)$$

while bases are largely restricted to metal hydroxides, which dissociate in solution according to:

$$NaOH(s) \rightarrow Na^+(aq) + OH^-(aq) \qquad (20\text{-}2)$$

These definitions are only applicable to water solutions. They also make it difficult to see why a compound such as ammonia, NH_3, can produce a basic solution in water. The more general model of Brønsted and Lowry identifies acids as proton donors and bases as proton acceptors, and treats all acid-base reactions as involving two reactants, one acid and one base. For our generic acid, then, the reaction that takes place is[1]:

$$HX(aq) + H_2O(l) \rightarrow H_3O^+(aq) + X^-(aq) \qquad (20\text{-}3)$$

For a strong base, one that contains hydroxide ions, the equation is essentially the same as equation (20-2), but for ammonia we have:

$$NH_3(aq) + H_2O(l) \rightleftharpoons NH_4^+(aq) + OH^-(aq) \qquad (20\text{-}4)$$

where the ammonium ion, $NH_4^+(aq)$ is the conjugate acid of the weak base NH_3 and hydroxide ion is the conjugate base of water, which acts as an acid by donating a proton to ammonia, leaving hydroxide ion in solution. Thus the general form of a Brønsted-Lowry acid base reaction is:

$$\text{acid} + \text{base} \rightleftharpoons \text{conjugate base} + \text{conjugate acid} \qquad (20\text{-}5)$$

We sometimes observe acidic and basic behavior for substances that we wouldn't normally identify as either acids or bases. It is those sorts of compounds that you will investigate in this experiment.

Prelaboratory Assignment

1. Read the entire experiment before you begin.

2. Prepare separate data tables for Parts A–C. You can do the same for the other parts as you go.

---

[1] H_3O^+ is the hydronium ion, essentially a hydrated hydrogen ion.

Prelaboratory Questions

1. In Part C of this experiment you are directed to test the pH of several solutions by placing some of the solution in a small beaker then testing with a pH probe. Why is it not a good idea to simply insert the probe into the stock bottle?

2. Ammonium chloride, NH_4Cl, is a salt consisting of the ammonium ion, NH_4^+, and chloride ion, Cl^-. As noted in the introduction, ammonium ion is the conjugate acid of the weak base NH_3, ammonia. As such, it should react with water to produce hydronium ion and ammonia. Write the equation for this reaction.

3. One of the reagents used in this experiment is hydroxylamine, $HONH_2$, which can be thought of as an ammonia molecule in which one of the three hydrogen atoms has been replaced by a hydroxyl group, H–O–, with the oxygen atom bonded directly to the central nitrogen atom.
   a. Draw the Lewis structure for hydroxylamine.
   b. The compound you will use, hydroxylammonium chloride, actually contains the conjugate acid of hydroxylamine. Like ammonium ion, hydroxylammonium forms when a hydrogen ion (proton) forms a coordinate covalent bond with the nitrogen atom of hydroxylamine. Draw the Lewis structure for hydroxylammonium ion.
   c. Write an equation similar to the one you wrote in Prelaboratory Question 2, showing the reaction that occurs when hydroxylammonium ion reacts with water, producing hydronium ion and hydroxylamine.

4. Would the solutions produced by the reactions in Prelaboratory Questions 2 and 3 be acidic, basic, or neutral? Explain.

5. a. Determine the volume of 0.50 M Na_2CO_3 needed to precipitate all of the calcium ion from a 10.0-mL sample of 0.10 M calcium chloride, $CaCl_2$, as calcium carbonate, $CaCO_3$.
   b. Determine the volume of 0.50 M HCl needed to convert the calcium carbonate from 5a to calcium hydrogen carbonate, $Ca(HCO_3)_2$.

Safety Precautions

1. Chemical splash-protective eyewear must be worn at all times in the laboratory.

2. Some of the reagents used in this experiment are toxic and/or corrosive to skin and clothing. Use care when handling them and wash your hands thoroughly with soap and water before leaving the laboratory.

Materials

Apparatus
beakers, 25–50 mL (several)
beaker, 100 mL
hot plate (or gas burner and stand)
test tubes, 150 mm or similar (several)
pH meter or interfaced pH probe

Reagents
calcium oxide, CaO
magnesium oxide, MgO
phenolphthalein
magnesium metal (ribbon or turnings)
chlorine water, $Cl_2(aq)$
0.50 M solutions of:
    sodium acetate, $NaC_2H_3O_2$
    sodium sulfate, Na_2SO_4
    sodium hydrogen sulfate, $NaHSO_4$
    sodium carbonate, Na_2CO_3
    sodium bicarbonate, $NaHCO_3$
    ammonium chloride, NH_4Cl
    hydroxylammonium chloride, $HONH_3Cl$
sodium hydroxide, NaOH(aq)
hydrochloric acid, HCl(aq)
0.10 M solutions of:
    aluminum chloride, $AlCl_3(aq)$
    calcium chloride, $CaCl_2(aq)$

Procedure

The steps that follow all involve observing the changes in pH and/or solubility that accompany various processes. For each step, your notebook record should describe what was done and what observations you made. It is not enough to just give the step number and describe the color or pH of the system.

For tests involving use of a pH meter or pH probe, it is essential that the tip of the probe be rinsed well with distilled or deionized water after each test. Failure to do so will result in collection of inappropriate data. Use a wash bottle to rinse the probe tip, catching the rinsings in a beaker.

Part A: Preliminary Tests

1. Place a few drops of 0.50 M hydrochloric acid, HCl(aq), in each of two test tubes. Add 2–3 drops of phenolphthalein to one tube and 2–3 drops of bromothymol blue indicator to the other. Note and record the results.

2. Repeat Step 1, but replace the 0.50 M HCl with 0.50 M NaOH. Test each with 2–3 drops of the two indicators; note and record the results.

3. Repeat the previous steps, but this time, add 2–3 drops of each indicator to separate samples of distilled or deionized water.

Part B: Metals and Metal Oxides

4. Place a pinch of calcium oxide in one small beaker or test tube and a pinch of magnesium oxide in another. Add about 15 mL of distilled or deionized water to each beaker and swirl to mix. Add a few drops of phenolphthalein indicator to each beaker. If no color appears, try warming each solution a bit, either with a burner or on a hot plate.

5. Place one or two pieces of magnesium (ribbon or turnings) in a 50-mL beaker that is about half-full of distilled or deionized water. Add a few drops of phenolphthalein. If no color change is observed, try warming the mixture gently, either with a burner or on a hot plate.

AP Experimental Chemistry

Part C: Nonmetals and Nonmetal Oxides

6. In a fume hood, put about 1 mL of chlorine water, $Cl_2(aq)$, in a small test tube and add a few drops of bromothymol blue.

7. Place about 10 mL of ice-cold seltzer (carbonated water) in a small beaker. Add a few drops of bromothymol blue indicator.

Part D: Salts Containing Conjugate Acids of Weak Bases and Conjugate Bases of Weak Acids

8. Using a pH meter if available, or pH test paper, try to determine the pH of 0.50 M solutions of each of the following salts: sodium acetate ($NaC_2H_3O_2$), sodium sulfate (Na_2SO_4), sodium hydrogen sulfate ($NaHSO_4$), sodium carbonate (Na_2CO_3), and sodium bicarbonate ($NaHCO_3$), also known as sodium hydrogen carbonate or baking soda. Place enough of each solution in a small beaker to cover the tip of your pH probe. If you are using pH indicator paper, about 5 mL should be enough.

9. Again using a pH meter or pH test paper, determine the pH of 1 M solutions of ammonium chloride, NH_4Cl, and hydroxylammonium chloride, $HONH_3Cl$.

10. Repeat the process of the previous steps using a 1 M solution of ammonium acetate, $NH_4C_2H_3O_2$.

Part E: Effect of pH on Solubility

11. To exactly 10.0 mL of 0.10 M $CaCl_2$, add the volume of 0.50 M Na_2CO_3 that you calculated in Prelaboratory Question **5a**. Stir, allowing the precipitate to settle, then determine the pH of the liquid above the precipitate.

    Now add the volume of 0.50 M HCl that you calculated in Prelaboratory Question **5b**. Your observations should include the results of both parts of this step. What is the pH of the mixture now?

Part F: Amphoteric Substances

12. Place 25 mL of 0.10 M aluminum chloride, $AlCl_3(aq)$, in a 100- or 150-mL beaker. Add 5.0 mL of 0.50 M NaOH(aq) and stir. Determine the pH of the resulting mixture.

13. Repeat the process two more times, adding 5.0-mL portions of 0.50 M NaOH, followed by stirring the mixture and determining its pH. At this point, all of the aluminum ion should have been precipitated as $Al(OH)_3(s)$.

14. Finally add a fourth 5.0-mL portion of 0.50 M NaOH. Determine the pH of the system and describe its appearance.

Analysis and Conclusions

Part A: Preliminary Tests

1. Make a table showing the color of each of the two indicators in acidic, neutral (distilled/deionized water), and basic solution.

Part B: Metals and Metal Oxides

2. Both magnesium metal and magnesium oxide produced pink colors, showing that hydroxide ion was produced by their respective reactions with water. Write balanced, complete ionic equations showing the reactions between magnesium and water to produce magnesium hydroxide and hydrogen gas and between magnesium oxide and water to produce magnesium hydroxide as the only product. Write a similar equation showing the reaction between calcium oxide and water.

Part C: Nonmetals and Nonmetal Oxides

3. Molecular chlorine reacts with water to produce a mixture of hydrochloric and hypochlorous acids. Write a balanced complete ionic equation for the reaction, bearing in mind that one of the two acid products is a weak acid.

4. Seltzer (carbonated water) is a solution of carbon dioxide in water. Based on the color you observed when you added bromothymol blue to seltzer, does carbon dioxide act as a Brønsted-Lowry acid or base? Write the appropriate equation for the reaction between CO_2 and H_2O.

Part D: Salts Containing Conjugate Acids of Weak Bases and Conjugate Bases of Weak Acids

5. a. Identify each of the solutions from step 8 as being acidic, basic, or neutral.
    b. Arrange the solutions in order of increasing pH.

6. a. For each of the acidic solutions, the anion is the conjugate base of a weak acid. Write equations showing each of these anions acting as a Brønsted-Lowry base as it reacts with water.
    b. For each of the basic solutions, the cation is the conjugate acid of a weak base. Write equations showing each of these cations acting as a Brønsted-Lowry acid as it reacts with water.

7. Ammonium acetate, $NH_4C_2H_3O_2$, consists of the conjugate acid of the weak base, ammonia, and the conjugate base of the weak acid, acetic acid. Based on the observed pH of the ammonium acetate solution, what can you conclude about the relative strengths of acetic acid and ammonia?

Part E: Effect of pH on Solubility

8. a. Write the *net* ionic equation for the reaction that took place when $Na_2CO_3(aq)$ was added to $CaCl_2(aq)$.
    b. You added just enough hydrochloric acid to the precipitate of calcium carbonate to convert all of the carbonate ion to hydrogen carbonate (bicarbonate). Write the complete ionic equation for this reaction.

Part F: Amphoteric Substances

9. In the original aluminum chloride solution, the aluminum cation is present in the form of a hexaaquo complex, $Al(H_2O)_6^{3+}$. The first three 5.0-mL additions of NaOH converted the soluble complex to insoluble aluminum hydroxide, $Al(OH)_3(s)$. Write the complete ionic equation for the conversion of hexaaquoaluminum to aluminum hydroxide.

10. The final 5.0-mL portion of 0.50 *M* NaOH produced a new, soluble complex of aluminum and hydroxide ions.
    a. What is the mole ratio of hydroxide to aluminum ion in this complex?
    b. Write the formula for the complex ion.

Experiment 21

Titration Curves

Objective

To make pH versus volume curves for three combinations of strong and weak acids and bases, including a diprotic acid

Concepts

Strong and weak acids and bases, pH curves, buffer systems, hydrolysis of ions

Introduction

Acid-base reactions involving strong acids and strong bases are often referred to as neutralization reactions. The term is valid because at the equivalence point the numbers of moles of hydrogen ion and hydroxide ion are equal, and the system is neutral, with a pH of 7. Such is not the case for titrations involving weak acids and/or weak bases.

To review, the terms *strong* and *weak*, as they apply to acids and bases, indeed to electrolytes in general, refer to the degree to which the acid or base is present as ions. Strong acids and bases are assumed to be 100% ionized (dissociated), so a 1.0 M solution of HNO_3 would be 1.0 molar in hydrogen ion (1.0 $M\,H^+$) and 1.0 molar in nitrate ion (1.0 $M\,NO_3^-$), and would contain no molecules of undissociated nitric acid (0.0 $M\,HNO_3$). Likewise, a 1.0 M solution of potassium hydroxide would have 1.0 mole K^+ and 1.0 mol OH^- per liter of solution, with no KOH molecules present in solution.

The percentage ionization for weak acids, such as acetic acid, CH_3COOH, is quite low. A 1.0 molar solution of acetic acid is only 0.4% ionized, so 99.6% of the acid is present as CH_3COOH molecules, with only 0.4% as H^+ and CH_3COO^- ions. The same situation arises with weak bases, such as aqueous ammonia, $NH_3(aq)$; the solution contains mostly ammonia molecules, with very little NH_4^+ or OH^- present.

As you know, the conjugate of a weak acid is itself a base, and the weaker the acid, the more strongly basic its conjugate will be. Acetate ion, the conjugate of acetic acid, will act as a base in the presence of water. This process is referred to as *hydrolysis*, and is illustrated in Equation *22-1*.

$$CH_3COO^-(aq) + H_2O(l) \rightarrow CH_3COOH(aq) + OH^-(aq) \qquad (22\text{-}1)$$

In similar fashion, the conjugate acids of weak bases will also undergo hydrolysis. For example, as shown in Equation *22-2*, ammonium ion, NH_4^+, the conjugate of ammonia, will act as an acid, donating a proton to a water molecule.

$$NH_4^+(aq) + H_2O(l) \rightarrow NH_3(aq) + H_3O^+(aq) \qquad (22\text{-}2)$$

At the equivalence point of a titration involving 1.0 M solutions of HNO_3 and KOH, the only ions present in the system are K^+ and NO_3^-, neither of which undergoes hydrolysis. On the other hand, at the equivalence point for a titration of 1.0 M solutions of ammonia, $NH_3(aq)$, and nitric acid, the system would contain equal numbers of moles of nitrate ion, NO_3^-, and ammonium ion, NH_4^+. While the nitrate ion would not interact with water, the ammonium ion would, as shown in Equation *22-2*, and the solution would have a pH below 7 as a result. A titration of acetic acid with potassium hydroxide, on the other hand, would have a pH greater than 7 at equivalence due to the hydrolysis of acetate ion, as shown in Equation *22-1*.

Sulfuric acid, H_2SO_4, is a typical *diprotic acid*, meaning it has two replaceable hydrogen atoms per molecule. Thus, when sulfuric acid is titrated against a strong base such as KOH, there are two sequential reactions taking place as shown in Equations *22-3* and *22-4*. Sulfuric acid is a strong acid, so the net ionic reaction, shown in Equation *22-3*, is typical of a strong acid–strong base system. Once that reaction is complete, however, and as addition of hydroxide ion continues, there is reaction between hydroxide and the relatively weak acid bisulfate, HSO_4^-. (See Equation *22-4*.)

$$H^+(aq) + OH^-(aq) \rightarrow H_2O(l) \qquad\qquad (22\text{-}3)$$

$$HSO_4^-(aq) + OH^-(aq) \rightarrow H_2O(l) + SO_4^{2-}(aq) \qquad\qquad (22\text{-}4)$$

In this experiment, you will carry out three titrations, all following the same basic sequence of steps. In the first two, you will verify the predictions of the preceding paragraphs by titrating 1.0 M HNO_3 and 1.0 M CH_3COOH with 1.0 M KOH, and 1.0 M sodium acetate, $NaC_2H_3O_2$, with 1.0 M HNO_3. Sodium acetate is a source of the weak base acetate ion, $C_2H_3O_2^-(aq)$. This third titration will differ from the first two in that you will be adding acid from a buret to a measured quantity of the base. Because you are starting with a basic solution, the pH will start high, then decrease as more and more acid is added. In each case you will monitor the pH of the system as a function of the volume of titrant added.

At your teacher's discretion, an optional fourth titration may be carried out using 0.50 M H_2SO_4 and 1.0 M KOH.

If you did Experiment 4, Analysis of Vinegar, you recall that it was necessary to standardize the base (KOH, in that experiment) against a primary standard, potassium hydrogen phthalate, KHP for short. In the present experiment, we are interested primarily in the shapes of the curves of pH versus volume of titrant, so standardization is not as necessary. This means, however, that the equivalence point for each titration may not occur at exactly the predicted volume ratio of titrant to analyte.

Prelaboratory Assignment

1. Read the entire experiment before coming to the laboratory.

2. Prepare data tables for each of the three titrations. In each case, you will be starting with 50.00 mL of the species to be titrated. You will need lines for the pH reading following each addition of the base, starting with 0.00 mL. If your teacher directs you to include the optional fourth titration, sulfuric acid with KOH, you will need a data table for it, as well.

Prelaboratory Questions

1. The value of K_a for acetic acid is 1.8 x 10^{-5}. Use this value to verify the percent ionization for 1.0 M CH_3COOH as given in the Introduction. Repeat for 0.10 M and 0.010 M CH_3COOH.

2. Determine the volume of titrant that you expect to need to reach the equivalence point in each of your titrations. (If you are to carry out the H_2SO_4-KOH titration, remember that there are two equivalence points for that one.)

3. Suggest an explanation for the fact that the concentration of sulfuric acid in the optional fourth titration is 0.50 M, while the concentrations of all other acids and bases are 1.0 M.

Safety Precautions

1. Chemical splash-protective eyewear must be worn at all times in the laboratory.

2. The solutions used in this experiment are corrosive to skin and clothing. Wipe up any and all spills with large volumes of water.

3. Aqueous ammonia has a harsh, unpleasant odor. The ammonia solution will readily release ammonia gas into the air. This not only exposes you and others to that odor, it also means that the concentration of the solution will slowly diminish over time. Keep containers of aqueous ammonia tightly closed when not in actual use.

Materials

Apparatus

buret, 50-mL
pH meter with pH electrode or other
    interface with pH probe
beaker, 150-mL (3 or 4)[1]
magnetic stirrer and stirring bar(s) (optional)[2]
400-mL (or larger) beaker for rinsing, waste

Reagents

nitric acid, HNO_3(aq), 1.0 M
potassium hydroxide, KOH(aq), 1.0 M
acetic acid, $HC_2H_3O_2$(aq), 1.0 M
sodium acetate, $NaC_2H_3O_2$(aq), 1.0 M
distilled or deionized water (wash bottle)

Procedure

Set up your pH meter or interfaced pH probe as shown in Figure 21-1. Set up your apparatus as shown below or as your teacher directs, if you are using a different type of pH measuring device, such as a calculator- or computer-interfaced probe.

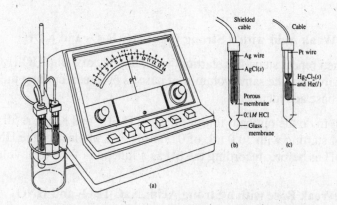

Figure 21-1. A typical stand-alone pH meter.

The same basic procedure applies to all of your titrations. If you are to perform the optional titration, it should follow the titrations of nitric and acetic acids, since all use the same KOH titrant.

Before your first titration, rinse the buret twice with distilled water, then rinse it twice with 1.0 M KOH. Be sure you rinse the tip of the buret as well as its barrel. Use your large beaker to collect all rinsings.

Fill the buret, including the tip, with 1.0 M KOH. Fill it past the 0.0-mL mark, then carefully run the volume down to 0.0. You are now ready for Part A.

---

[1] Assumes a fresh beaker for each titration, but beakers can be washed between trials. If they are, they should be rinsed with distilled water and dried before the next titration.
[2] If you do not have a magnetic stirrer, you will need to swirl the beaker after each addition of titrant, or use a stirring rod to stir the contents.

Part A: Titration of a Strong Acid with a Strong Base: HNO_3 and KOH

1. Place 30.0 mL of 1.0 M HNO_3 in a clean 150-mL beaker. Place the beaker on the magnetic stirrer, add the stirring bar, and begin the stirrer. Carefully lower the pH probe into the solution, taking care to position it so that the tip is not struck by the stirring bar. When the pH reading is stable, note and record the pH of the system for 0.00 mL of base added.

2. Add 10.00 mL of 1.0 M KOH from the buret and allow the solutions to mix thoroughly. When the pH is steady, record the volume of base added and the pH of the mixture.

3. Add 5.00-mL of the KOH solution. Allow the pH reading to become steady, then record the pH and the total volume of base added, 15.00 mL. Continue adding two more 5.00-mL samples of the KOH, recording the appropriate data after each addition, until a total of 25.0 mL has been added. After each addition, enter the total volume of base.

   Now begin to add the base 1.0 mL at a time, recording the total volume of base and the pH after each addition, until the total amount of base added reaches 35.0 mL. Follow with one final 5.00-mL addition and record the final volume and pH.

4. Raise the pH probe or electrode out of the solution and use your distilled-water wash bottle to rinse it thoroughly, catching the rinsings in the beaker containing your titration products. If you need to reuse your 150-mL beaker, place the contents in your large beaker and reserve it for **Disposal.**

Part B: Titration of a Weak Acid with a Strong Base: $HC_2H_3O_2$ and KOH

5. Refill your buret, then repeat steps 1–4 starting with 30.0 mL of 1.0 M $HC_2H_3O_2$, in place of the HNO_3 used previously. Use the same volumes of base as before, recording the pH as a function of the total volume of base added.

Note: If you are going to do the optional fourth titration, H_2SO_4 and KOH, refill your buret and repeat steps 1–4 starting with 30.0 mL of 0.50 M H_2SO_4 in place of the HNO_3. Use the same volumes of KOH as before, recording the pH as a function of the total volume of base added.

Part C: Titration of a Weak Base with a Strong Acid: $NaC_2H_3O_2$ and HNO_3

6. Empty your buret into your waste beaker. Wash it thoroughly with soap and water and rinse it with tap water, and then twice with distilled water, being sure to rinse the tip as well as the barrel of the buret. Rinse twice with 5–10 mL portions of 1.0 M nitric acid, then fill the buret with 1.0 M HNO_3 and adjust the level to 0.0 mL. CAUTION: Nitric acid may stain skin and clothes.

7. Place 30.0 mL of 1.0 M $NaC_2H_3O_2$ in a clean 150-mL beaker. Place the beaker on the magnetic stirrer, add the stirring bar, and begin the stirrer. Carefully lower the pH probe into the solution, taking care to position it so that the tip is not struck by the stirring bar. When the pH reading is stable, note and record the pH of the system for 0.00 mL of acid added.

8. Add 10.00 mL of 1.0 M HNO_3 from the buret, and allow the solutions to mix thoroughly. When the pH is steady, record the volume of base added and the pH of the mixture.

9. Add 5.00-mL of the KOH solution. Allow the pH reading to become steady, then record the pH and the total volume of base added, 15.00 mL. Continue adding two more 5.00-mL samples of the HNO_3, recording the appropriate data after each addition, until a total of 25.0 mL has been added. After each addition, enter the total volume of acid.

Now begin to add the acid 1.0 mL at a time, recording the total volume of base and the pH after each addition, until the total amount of base added reaches 35.0 mL. Follow with one final 5.00 mL addition and record the final volume and pH.

Disposal

1. As you have after each titration, raise the pH sensor out of the titration vessel and use your distilled-water wash bottle to rinse it, catching the rinsings in the beaker. After it has been cleaned, consult your teacher as to what you are to do with all electronic equipment.

2. Allow any remaining titrant to drain from your buret into the waste beaker. Since two of your three titrations wound up with an excess of KOH, it is likely (but not certain) that the contents of your waste beaker are basic. Test this by adding a few drops of an indicator such as bromothymol blue or phenolphthalein. If, as expected, the system is basic, add small amounts of HNO_3 (or another acid, such as vinegar) until the color of the indicator changes. The resulting mixture may be rinsed down the drain with large amounts of water. If the solution is not basic, check using pH paper to see if it is acidic. If acidic, neutralize by adding solid sodium bicarbonate until no bubbles are produced upon further addition of $NaHCO_3$, and then rinse down the drain with large amounts of water.

3. Wash your buret with soap and water, then rinse first with tap water and then with two 5–10 mL portions of distilled water. Clamp the buret, with the stopcock open, in an inverted (tip up) position and allow it to drain dry.

Processing the Data

For each of the titrations, you are to make a separate plot of pH (vertical axis) versus Volume of Titrant (mL) (horizontal axis). In each case, identify the equivalence point for the titration by making a mark on the curve. The equivalence point in each case is the point of inflection. For those cases in which base was being added to acid, it will be where the slope of the graph stops increasing and begins to decrease. For the titration involving sodium acetate and nitric acid, the reverse is true. Consult your text for examples.

If you are using a computer-interfaced or calculator-interfaced pH probe, you may have software that will make the plots and identify the equivalence points for you. The same is true if you are using more stand-alone devices, such as LabQuest or PasPort.

If you are making your own graphs, draw the best-fit smooth curve that you can through the data points. A device known as a French curve may be useful for this.

Analysis and Conclusions

1. Make and complete a table with the headings shown below. By "half-equivalence" is meant the point at which you had added half the volume of titrant that was needed to reach equivalence.

	HNO$_3$/KOH	HC$_2$H$_3$O$_2$/KOH	NaC$_2$H$_3$O$_2$/HNO$_3$
pH at equivalence			
vol. of titrant needed to reach equivalence			
pH at half-equivalence			
vol. of titrant needed to reach half-equivalence			

2. Write the net ionic equations for each of the three titration reactions that you conducted: HNO$_3$/KOH, HC$_2$H$_3$O$_2$/KOH, and NaC$_2$H$_3$O$_2$/HNO$_3$. (Hint: Consider the species that were present in the sodium acetate solution before you began addition of nitric acid.)

3. Use the pH values that you recorded to determine the concentration of all ions present initially, at half-equivalence, and at equivalence for the titration of nitric acid with KOH.

4. Repeat the calculations of question 2 for: (a) the titration of acetic acid by KOH, and (b) the titration of sodium acetate by HNO$_3$.

5. The Henderson-Hasselbalch equation was originally derived for use with buffer systems such as arise in biochemistry so often, but it also describes the effect of concentration on the relationship between pH and pK_a for a weak acid being titrated with a strong base. It has the form:

$$pH = pK_a + \log \frac{[A^-]}{[HA]}$$

where $[HA]$ and $[A^-]$ represent the molar concentrations of a weak acid, HA, and its conjugate base, A$^-$. When your titration of acetic acid with KOH has reached the half-equivalence point, we can assume that $[HA] = [A^-]$. Explain: (a) why this is a valid assumption, (b) what that means for pH and pK_a, and (c) the extent to which your experimental result agrees with the predictions made by the Henderson-Hasselbalch equation.

6. The Henderson-Hasselbalch equation can also be applied to titrations of a weak base with a strong acid, such as the reaction between acetate ion and nitric acid. In this case, at the half-equivalence point the system contains equal amounts of acetate ion and acetic acid molecules, and the pH of the system should equal the value of pK_a for acetic acid. Given that K_a for HC$_2$H$_3$O$_2$ is 1.8 x 10^{-5}, how well does your experimental result match the predictions of the Henderson-Hasselbalch equation?

7. In all probability, your experimental results will not exactly match prediction. Whether you got a close match or not, discuss the likely sources of variation from expected behavior that are present in this experiment.

Experiment 22

Acids, Bases, and Buffers

Introduction

In the earlier experiment *Analysis of Vinegar*, you used a strong base, sodium hydroxide, NaOH, to determine the concentration of acetic acid in ordinary vinegar. You are going to investigate the same system once again, but this time the indicator will be replaced by a pH meter or with a pH probe connected to an interface. Acetic acid is a weak acid; that is, only a very small percentage of the acetic acid molecules are present in ionic form at any one time. The principal species in the solution are acetic acid molecules, not hydrogen and acetate ions. The equilibrium dissociation is a *reversible reaction*, and is represented by a double arrow, and the position of equilibrium lies strongly to the left. Thus:

$$HC_2H_3O_2(aq) \rightleftharpoons H^+(aq) + C_2H_3O_2^-(aq) \qquad (22\text{--}1)$$

As discussed in Chapter 14, the pH scale serves as a measure of the concentration of hydrogen ions in an aqueous solution. We represent this concentration by $[H^+]$, with the square brackets understood to refer to the concentration (molarity) of the ion or molecule they enclose. As noted above, acetic acid is a weak acid, so relatively few hydrogen ions are present in solution at any given time and the pH is not as low as it would be for a solution of a strong acid, such as hydrochloric acid, HCl, which is 100% dissociated.

Because the acetate ion, $C_2H_3O_2^-$, has a strong tendency to combine with hydrogen ions, as shown by equation (22–1), above, we can think of acetate as acting as a base; that is, it acts as a proton acceptor. If you could produce a solution that contained acetate ions without the hydrogen ions, you would expect it to be basic; that is, it should have a pH greater than 7.00. Sodium acetate, $NaC_2H_3O_2$, is a strong electrolyte. It is totally dissociated into ions when dissolved in water.

$$NaC_2H_3O_2(s) \xrightarrow{\;100\%\;} Na^+(aq) + C_2H_3O_2^-(aq) \qquad (22\text{--}2)$$

As you might expect, solutions of sodium acetate are mildly alkaline, or basic, due to the tendency of the acetate ions to take a proton from water. This process is known as *hydrolysis* and represents a state of dynamic equilibrium, similar to reaction (22–1), above.

$$C_2H_3O_2^-(aq) + H_2O(l) \rightleftharpoons HC_2H_3O_2(aq) + OH^-(aq) \qquad (22\text{--}3)$$

An interesting type of mixture, which you will investigate in this experiment, is called a *buffer*. Buffers are of two types. An acidic buffer consists of a weak acid, such as acetic acid, mixed with a compound that contains the conjugate base of the acid (e.g., acetic acid, $HC_2H_3O_2$, and sodium acetate, $NaC_2H_3O_2$, which acts as a source of acetate ion, $C_2H_3O_2^-$). A basic buffer consists of a weak base, such as ammonia, $NH_3(aq)$, and a compound that contains the cationic form of the base (in this case, NH_4^+, from a salt such as NH_4Cl).

You will prepare an acidic buffer, consisting of acetic acid and sodium acetate, to see how the buffered system responds when aqueous sodium hydroxide is added. You will compare this result with the behavior you observe when the sodium hydroxide is added to a solution that contains only acetic acid.

In order to help you track the progress of your titrations, you will either use a stand-alone pH meter or a hand-held interface, such as LabPro™, CBL2™, or LabQuest™. Your teacher will tell you what your instrumentation will be and will direct you as to the proper means to set up, operate, and care for the equipment.

Prelaboratory Assignment

1. Read the entire experiment before you begin.

2. Because this experiment uses the same basic setup as the previous one, Experiment 21: *Titration Curves*, you should review that experiment as well.

3. Prepare a Data Table in your notebook in which to record the titration data for Part 1; data tables for the later parts can be made as needed.

Prelaboratory Questions

1. Calculate the mass of sodium acetate you would need to prepare 30.0 mL of 0.10 M $NaC_2H_3O_2$ solution. Show your calculations.

2. Acids are proton donors; bases are proton acceptors. In these definitions, the "protons" are actually hydrogen ions. Why are hydrogen ions referred to as protons?

3. **a.** Acetic acid is a weak acid. Write the Brønsted-Lowry equation for the reaction between water and molecular acetic acid to produce hydronium ion and acetate ion. Identify the conjugate acid-base pairs in your equation.

   b. Ammonia is a weak base. Write the Brønsted-Lowry equation for the reaction between ammonia and water. Identify the conjugate acid-base pairs in your equation.

   c. Would a solution of ammonium chloride, NH_4Cl, be expected to have a pH less than, greater than, or equal to 7.00? Write a chemical equation defending your choice. What are the principal species present in such a solution?

Safety Precautions

1. Chemical splash-protective eyewear must be worn at all times in the laboratory.

2. Sodium hydroxide is corrosive to skin and clothing. Clean up spills with large amounts of water.

Materials

Apparatus
buret, 50-mL
pH meter with pH probe or other
    interface with pH probe
beaker, 150-mL (2)
magnetic stirrer and stirring bar (optional)[1]
250-mL (or larger) beaker, for rinsing
safety goggles

Reagents
acetic acid, $HC_2H_3O_2$, 0.10 M
sodium hydroxide, NaOH, 0.10 M
sodium acetate, $NaC_2H_3O_2$, solid
distilled water (wash bottle)
hydrochloric acid, HCl, 0.10 M

---

[1] If you do not have a magnetic stirrer, you will need to swirl the beaker after each addition of NaOH or use a glass stirring rod to stir the contents.

Procedure

1. Set up your pH meter or interfaced pH probe as shown in Figure 22-1, next page. Set up your apparatus as shown, or as your teacher directs if you are using a different type of pH measuring device, such as a calculator- or computer-interfaced probe.

Part A: Titration of Acetic Acid by Sodium Hydroxide

2. Rinse the buret with a few milliliters of 0.10 M NaOH; be sure to rinse the barrel and the tip of the buret. Discard the rinsings in your waste beaker, then fill the buret with fresh NaOH.

3. Place 30.0 mL of 0.10 M HC$_2$H$_3$O$_2$ in the beaker. Place the beaker on the magnetic stirrer and begin the stirrer. Carefully lower the pH probe into the solution, taking care to position it so that it is not struck by the stirring bar.

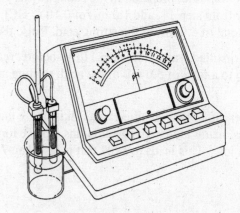

Figure 22-1. A typical stand-alone pH meter.

4. Add 10.00 mL of 0.10 M NaOH from the buret and allow the solutions to mix thoroughly. When the pH is steady, record volume of base added and the pH of the mixture.

5. Add 5.00 mL of the NaOH solution. Allow the pH reading to become steady, then record the pH and the total volume of base added, 15.00 mL. Continue adding two more 5.00-mL samples of the NaOH, recording the appropriate data after each addition, until a total of 25.0 mL has been added. After each addition, enter the total volume of base.

   Now begin to add the base 1.0 mL at a time, recording the total volume of base and the pH after each addition, until the total amount of base added reaches 35.0 mL. Follow with one final 5.00-mL addition and record the final volume and pH.

6. Follow the directions for Part A in **Disposal**.

Part B: Preparing and Titrating the Buffer

7. Weigh out the mass of solid sodium acetate you calculated in prelaboratory question 3. Place the solid in one of your two 150-mL beakers. Add 30.0 mL of distilled water and swirl or mix until all of the solid has dissolved. (Dissolving is endothermic, so this may take a few minutes; use the magnetic stirrer, if you have one.)

   In your other beaker, dissolve the same mass of solid sodium acetate in 30.0 mL of the 0.10 M acetic acid. As before, swirl or mix until all of the solid has dissolved. This is the buffer system that you will compare to the unbuffered acid.

8. Use the pH probe to determine the pH of the solution of sodium acetate in distilled water. Record the value. Rinse the pH probe with distilled water, catching the rinsings in your waste beaker.

9. Place the beaker containing the acetic acid/sodium acetate mixture on the magnetic stirrer and place the pH probe in the solution, taking care that the stirring bar cannot strike and damage the probe.

10. Refill the buret with 0.10 M NaOH and titrate the buffer in the same way that you did the acetic acid, steps 3–5.

Part C: Effect of Acid on the Buffer

11. Clean your two titration beakers as you did after Part 1. Fill one with 30.0 mL of distilled water and the other with 30.0 mL of buffer mixture, prepared in the same way as you did for Part B.

12. To the beaker containing the buffer from step 11, add 1.0 mL of 0.10 M HCl; read and record the pH. Repeat four more times, for a total of 5.0 mL of the strong acid. Rinse the probe thoroughly.

13. Repeat step 12 using the beaker of distilled water from step 11. As before, read the initial pH, then add 1.0 mL of 0.10 M HCl, up to a total of 5.0 mL of the acid, reading and recording the pH after each addition.

Note: If you are using deionized water rather than distilled water, it is likely that the pH will not be 7.00. In removing metal cations, many ion-exchange columns replace ions such as calcium and magnesium with hydrogen ions. This leads to a pH that is less than 7.00.

Disposal

Part A

1. Raise the pH probe from the titration beaker and replace that beaker with your waste beaker. Use the wash bottle to rinse the probe, catching the rinsings in the waste beaker.

2. The contents of the titration beaker is mildly basic, but it is safe to rinse it down the drain with large amounts of water. Remove the stirring bar, then rinse the beaker well, first with tap water and then with distilled water. It is now ready for use in Part B.

3. Rinse the stirring bar with distilled water. Dry it before reuse.

Part B

4. Follow the instructions for Part 1, rinsing all solutions down the drain. Clean the beakers with tap water and distilled water and return them to their proper location.

5. Rinse the stirring bar with distilled water, dry it and return it to where it belongs.

6. Drain the buret into your waste beaker. Add a drop of phenolphthalein to the contents of the beaker. If the indicator turns pink, as is likely, add acetic acid, a few milliliters at a time, until the pink just disappears. The contents of the beaker may now safely be rinsed down the drain.

7. Rinse the buret several times with tap water, then with distilled water, being careful to rinse both the barrel and the tip of the buret. Clamp the buret in the inverted position over paper towels so that it can drain.

Part C

8. If the pH of the solution in your beaker is between 5 and 7, it can be rinsed down the drain with excess water. If it is below 5, add 0.10 M NaOH until the system is in the desired range. This should take very little of the base, so add the NaOH only in small quantities.

9. Return the pH apparatus to the location designated by your teacher.

Analysis and Conclusions

1. Plot your data for each of the two titrations (Parts A and B). Take the time to make a smooth curve; part of your grade will reflect the quality of your graph.

2. Describe the difference between the shapes of the graphs for the buffered and unbuffered systems as they are titrated with sodium hydroxide.

3. Account for the effect of small quantities of a strong acid on the buffered system. Why does the pH not change as rapidly for the buffer as it did for distilled water? What species was consuming the acid?

4. Write net-ionic equations for:
   a. The reaction that occurred in the titrations in Part A and B (Hint: it is the same reaction in both cases.)
   b. The reaction that occurred when HCl was added to the buffer in Part C

5. At what pH did the sign of the slope of your graph for Part 1 change from (+) to (-)? This is known as the *inflection point* of the curve and it is the equivalence point for the titration. Account for the fact that this point is not at pH 7. What were the principal species in the solution at that point?

6. At what pH did the sign of the slope of your graph for the titration of sodium acetate appear to change from (+) to (-)? Account for your result. What were the principal species in the solution at that point?

Experiment 23

Conductivity Titrations

Objective

To determine the stoichiometry of a precipitation reaction by conductivity titration

Concepts

Precipitation reactions, conductivity of electrolyte solutions, stoichiometry

Introduction

Acid-base reactions are commonly studied by titrations in which the progress of the reaction is monitored by using a pH meter. On the other hand, if the goal is simply to determine when the reaction is complete, an indicator can be used. Recall that indicators are compounds that change color when the pH of the system reaches a certain value. In precipitation reactions, it is the formation of an insoluble solid that is the driving force; the pH may not change at all.

In precipitation reactions what does change is the total number of ions in the system. The more ions there are, the better the solution is able to conduct an electric current. So, one way to monitor such a reaction is by observing changes in the *conductivity* of the system.

The reaction you will study in this experiment is the one that occurs when a dilute oxalic acid solution is added to a solution of lead(II) acetate. Like many compounds containing the lead(II) ion, lead(II) oxalate has a low solubility. Also, acetate is a stronger base than the oxalate ion. Thus, mixing solutions of lead(II) acetate and oxalic acid results in the formation of a white precipitate of lead(II) oxalate, PbC_2O_4, along with the weak acid, $HC_2H_3O_2$. Because you are going from strong electrolyte to weak acid and insoluble ionic salt, the conductivity drops steadily, reaching a minimum at the equivalence point. Beyond the equivalence point the conductivity increases again.

Your teacher will provide you with solutions of oxalic acid and lead(II) acetate. You will measure the initial conductivity of the solution, then add small amounts of oxalic acid, $H_2C_2O_4$, measuring the conductance after each addition. The molecular equation for the reaction that takes place is:

$$Pb(C_2H_3O_2)_2(aq) + H_2C_2O_4(aq) \rightarrow PbC_2O_4(s) + 2HC_2H_3O_2(aq) \qquad (23\text{-}1)$$

Conductivity probes are designed to measure the electrical conductivity of a solution, and so can be used to see how the conductivity changes as one reactant is added to another. In this system, the lead(II) oxalate precipitates from the solution, and the other product (acetic acid) is a weak acid and thus has very low conductivity. Therefore, the ability of the solution to conduct an electric current should reach a minimum when the number of moles of lead(II) ion originally present is equal to the number of moles of oxalic acid added. This point is known as the *equivalence point*.

Prelaboratory Assignment

1. Read the entire experiment before you begin.

2. Prepare a data table for recording the conductivity readings corresponding to each addition of oxalic acid, starting with 0.0 mL volume.

Prelaboratory Questions

1. The equation for the reaction you are investigating is given in molecular form in the Introduction. Present the same reaction as:
    a. A complete ionic equation (assume the oxalic acid dissociates into two hydrogen ions an oxalate ion)
    b. A net-ionic equation

2. Why is it necessary to filter out the precipitated solid remaining after the completion of the experiment?

3. The lead(II) acetate solution has an approximate concentration of $0.010\ M$. What volume of 0.10 M oxalic acid should be needed to reach the equivalence point? Show calculations to defend your prediction.

Safety Precautions

1. Chemical splash-protective eyewear must be worn at all times in the laboratory.

2. Lead compounds are very toxic. Avoid all contact with the lead(II) acetate solution and with the solution in the beaker after the reaction. Gloves are recommended.

3. Oxalic acid, even in low concentration, is corrosive to skin and clothing.

4. Clean up all spills with large amounts of water.

Materials

Apparatus
apparatus and probe
    for conductance determination
100-mL beakers (2)
0.50-mL volumetric or Mohr pipet,
    buret, or calibrated plastic micropipet
    for adding oxalic acid
magnetic stirrer and stirring bar, if available
ring stand and iron ring
funnel
filter paper

Reagents
lead(II) acetate, 0.010M(aq)
0.10 M oxalic acid, $H_2C_2O_4$(aq)
distilled water (wash bottle)

Procedure

1. Set up the conductivity apparatus as directed by your teacher.

2. Place the stirring bar in the beaker and add 20.0 mL of lead(II) acetate solution. Place the beaker on the stirrer and start the bar spinning; adjust the rate so that the surface of the liquid just barely shows a vortex. Carefully lower the probe so that it is submerged in the solution but is not in danger of being struck by the stirring bar. Take your first reading; this is your 0.00-mL reading.

3. Use the pipet (or buret) to add 0.50 mL of the 0.10 M oxalic acid. Read the conductivity again; this time, for 0.50-mL.

4. Take additional readings after each addition of 0.50 mL of the acid solution. Continue in this fashion until you have added a total of 4.00 mL, or until the conductivity has risen to the level of the initial (0.00 mL) reading.

Disposal

1. Raise the probe from the mixture in the beaker. Use the wash bottle to rinse the probe with distilled water. Allow the rinsings to fall into the beaker.

2. Use metal forceps or tweezers to remove the stirring bar from the beaker. Hold it over the beaker while you rinse it with the wash bottle.

3. Set up for filtration, using an iron ring and ring stand. Place your second beaker under the funnel, then filter the mixture in the beaker where the reaction took place. To do this, swirl the contents to make a slurry of the precipitate, then pour into the filter.

4. When filtration is complete, carefully remove the filter with the lead(II) oxalate precipitate from the funnel and place it in the location designated by your teacher.

5. The filtrate (liquid) in the receiver beaker contains a very dilute solution of acetic acid and can be rinsed down the drain safely using large amounts of water.

6. Wash both beakers, the stirring bar, and any other apparatus that came in contact with the lead solution or precipitate. Use soap and water.

7. After removing your gloves, wash your hands thoroughly with soap and water.

Analysis and Conclusions

1. Use graph paper to plot your data of conductivity versus volume of $H_2C_2O_4$. (Note: If you are using an interfaced probe system, the interface may do this for you. Consult your teacher.) Assume that the lines showing the conductivity are straight. Extend each so that the two intersect. The intersection point is your experimental value for the equivalence point of the reaction. Be sure to label the axes.

2. Describe the shape of the curve. Include a description of the relative slopes of the two intersecting lines.

3. Identify the volume of $H_2C_2O_4$ that was needed to reach the equivalence point. (This may or may not be a whole number, and almost certainly will not coincide with any of your data points.)

4. Compare the value from the preceding question with your prediction in prelaboratory question 3. Suggest a possible explanation for any significant difference.

5. There are two products to the reaction: lead(II) oxalate, which is insoluble, and acetic acid, which is a weak electrolyte. Account for the fact that once the equivalence point is reached, the conductivity increases again as $H_2C_2O_4$ is added.

6. As you add the oxalic acid and precipitate the lead(II) ion from solution as $PbC_2O_4(s)$, you are not changing the total amount of lead(II) ion present in the system.
   a. Use the volume and molarity of the oxalic acid to determine the number of moles of oxalate ion added at the equivalence point.
   b. The result from a. must also be the number of moles of lead(II) ion that were present. Why?
   c. Use the number of moles of lead(II) ion that were present in the 20.0 mL of the lead(II) acetate solution to calculate the actual molarity of the original lead(II) acetate solution.

Experiment 24

Le Chatelier's Principle

Objective

To observe the shifts in equilibrium position predicted by Le Chatelier's principle and to interpret those shifts in terms of the concentration changes involved

Concepts

Equilibrium systems and Le Chatelier's principle

Introduction

Le Chatelier's Principle describes the effect that applying various types of stress has on the position of a system at equilibrium, that is, whether it will shift to increase or decrease the concentration(s) of products in the equilibrium system. The basic idea that Le Chatelier proposed is that when a system at equilibrium is subjected to a stress, it will shift in such a way as to relieve the effects of that stress.

Stresses include variations in the concentrations of reactants or products, changes in the temperature of the system, and (for reactions involving gases) the pressure. Of these, only a change in temperature actually changes the value of the equilibrium constant.

Most of our investigations occur in open systems, usually in aqueous solution. Unless gases are involved in the reaction, the volume of the system is just the volume of the solution, and pressure is of little or no consequence. This permits us to simplify Le Chatelier's Principle to read:

> *For any reaction system at equilibrium in solution:*
> * *If you add a reactant or a product to the system, it will try to consume what was added.*
> * *If you remove a reactant or a product from the system, it will try to replace what was removed.*

In this experiment you will observe what Le Chatelier's Principle means. Your investigation will deal with two complex ions, both containing cobalt(II); they are $Co(H_2O)_6^{2+}$ and $CoCl_4^{2}$. The procedure is short and should not require more than 20 minutes to complete. The key is to understand what stresses were applied, how the system responded, and why it responded as it did.

Prelaboratory Assignment

1. Read the entire experiment before coming to the laboratory.

2. Prepare a two-column table in your notebook with the headings: Action, and System Response. For each of the procedure steps 5–8, as you perform the action called for, write what was done in the "Action" column and describe what you observe under "System Response."

Prelaboratory Questions

1. The formula for solid cobalt(II) chloride is $CoCl_2 \cdot 6H_2O$. What name do we give to compounds that have water molecules bound to them?

2. a. Write the equation for dissolving calcium chloride in water.
   b. Use Le Chatelier's Principle to predict the effect of the addition of solid calcium chloride to a solution containing both of the cobalt complexes.

3. a. Write the equation for dissolving silver nitrate in water.
   b. Write the equation for the precipitation reaction that you would expect when a solution containing silver ions is added to a solution containing chloride ions.

Safety Precautions

1. Chemical splash-protective eyewear must be worn at all times in the laboratory.

2. Cobalt and silver solutions are mildly toxic, so you must wash your hands thoroughly before leaving the laboratory.

3. Silver nitrate will stain skin and clothing. Wipe up all spills with large amounts of water.

4. Concentrated hydrochloric acid will attack skin and clothing. Neutralize acid spills on laboratory surfaces before wiping up.

5. Be careful using the hot plate. Remember that hot surfaces look the same as cool ones. Use a hot pad to transfer hot containers from the hot plate.

Materials

Apparatus
50-mL beaker
Shell vials, 1 dram (5)
hot plate
ice bath

Reagents
cobalt chloride hexahydrate, $CoCl_2 \cdot 6H_2O(s)$
ethanol (or methanol, or 2-propanol)
12 M hydrochloric acid, $HCl(aq)$
calcium chloride pellets, $CaCl_2(s)$
acetone
silver nitrate solution, $AgNO_3(aq)$, 0.10 M

Procedure

1. Thoroughly dry your 50-ml beaker with a paper towel, then use the markings on the side to measure about 25–30 ml of ethanol into the beaker.

2. Examine the solid cobalt(II) chloride, noting both its color and the formula for the compound, as shown on the label of the stock bottle.

3. Place a small sample of the solid (about the volume of two drops of water) in the beaker of ethanol and swirl to dissolve the solid. Note the color of the solution.

4. Divide most of the solution among five flat-bottomed vials, leaving about 0.5 cm of the solution in the beaker. The actual volume in each vial is not important but the volumes in each should all be approximately equal.

5. To one of the vials, add five drops of distilled water, one drop at a time, recording observations after each drop. Duplicate the process with each of four other vials, so that all five are the same color.

   Use four of the five for Step 6, retaining one as a control for comparison purposes.

6. a. Take one of the vials from Step 5 to the fume hood. Use the dropper provided with the acid to CAREFULLY add five drops of concentrated hydrochloric acid, one drop at a time, to the solution in the vial.

   b. To a second vial from Step 5, add 2–3 small pellets of solid calcium chloride.

   c. To the third vial, add 3–4 drops of acetone.

   d. To your fourth vial, add 10 drops of 0.1 M silver nitrate, $AgNO_3$, one drop at a time.

7. Return the contents of your control vial to the beaker containing the remainder of the original alcohol solution of cobalt(II) chloride. Add just enough distilled water to get a color that is about half-way between the blue and pink shades you have observed so far. This solution should have approximately equal amounts of the two complex ions. Place the beaker on a hot plate and warm it until vapors can be seen rising from the surface, about 50°C. Note the change in solution color.

8. Finally, chill the beaker in an ice bath to see whether the color change in Step 7 is reversible.

Analysis and Conclusions

The net-ionic equation for the equilibrium reaction you have been investigating is

$$Co(H_2O)_6^{2+}(aq) + 4Cl^-(aq) \rightleftharpoons CoCl_4^{2-}(aq) + 6H_2O(l)$$ (24–1)

pink   blue

1. **a.** Which cobalt complex was favored by addition of water to the solution of cobalt(II) chloride in alcohol?

    b. Use Le Chatelier's Principle to explain the color change you observed.

2. **a.** Which cobalt complex was favored in both procedure steps 6a and 6b?

    b. What ion is common to both of the reagents you used to bring about the color changes in these two steps?

    c. Use Le Chatelier's Principle to explain why the color changes occurred in each case.

3. Acetone absorbs water. Use this fact and Le Chatelier's Principle to explain the color change that you saw when you added acetone to the third vial in Step 6.

4. Silver chloride, AgCl, is a white solid. The equilibrium constant for formation of this precipitate is $K_f = 6 \times 10^9$; the reaction is:

    $$Ag^+(aq) + Cl^-(aq) \rightleftharpoons AgCl(s)$$ (24–2)

    a. At equilibrium, would you expect to have mostly silver and chloride ions in solution, or mostly solid silver chloride? Explain.

    b. What color was the precipitate produced in Step 6d? What must the precipitate have been?

    c. What color did the liquid in the vial turn? Which complex of cobalt was favored? Explain.

    d. Use Le Chatelier's Principle to explain why the liquid in the vial underwent the color change.

5. **a.** Which cobalt complex was favored by addition of energy as heat? Which complex was favored by cooling?

    b. The value of ΔH for the process represented by equation *24–1* is +50kJ/mol. Rewrite equation *24–1* with the energy term included in the equation.

    c. Use Le Chatelier's Principle and the equation from **5b** to explain the color changes that resulted from the heating and cooling.

6. Of the various "stresses" that you applied to the system in this experiment, the only one that actually changes the value of the equilibrium constant is a change in temperature. As you know, an increase in temperature increases the rate of a reaction. For a system at equilibrium, it can be shown that an increase in temperature tends to bring about a greater increase in the rate of the endothermic direction than it does for the exothermic direction. As a solution of cobalt(II) chloride in a mixture of ethanol and water is warmed from 0°C to 50°C, what happens to the concentrations of the two complex ions of cobalt?

AP Experimental Chemistry

Experiment 25

Determination of an Equilibrium Constant

Objective

To determine experimentally the value of an equilibrium constant by colorimetric means

Concepts

Equilibrium, colorimetry, complex ions

Introduction

In Chapter 13 you were introduced to one of the most important concepts in all of chemistry: chemical equilibrium. At equilibrium, reactants are being converted to products at exactly the same rate as products are changing back into reactants. This is a dynamic state; although no apparent changes are occurring, in fact there is constant change taking place. The double arrow indicates that the reaction is proceeding in both directions simultaneously.

$$\text{reactants} \rightleftharpoons \text{products} \tag{25-1}$$

As long as the temperature of the system remains constant, the relative numbers of reactant and product particles (molecules, ions, etc.) remain constant. This relation is expressed by means of an *equilibrium constant, K,* and takes the form:

$$K = \frac{[\text{products}]^n}{[\text{reactants}]^m} \tag{25-2}$$

where the square brackets indicate that we are referring to the molar concentrations of the reactants and products. The superscripts, *m* and *n*, relate to the stoichiometry of the system. This is a mathematical representation of Le Chatelier's principle.

An equilibrium state is produced when iron(III) ions, Fe^{3+}(aq), and thiocyanate ions, SCN^-(aq), are present together in aqueous solution. The pale-yellow iron(III) ions and the colorless thiocyanate ions combine to form a blood-red complex, known as the thiocyanatoiron(III), $FeSCN^{2+}$(aq). Notice that the complex is charged; because a cation with a +3 charge has joined with an anion that carries a -1 charge, the net charge on the resulting combination is +2. The equilibrium may be represented in equation form as:

$$Fe^{3+}(aq) + SCN^-(aq) \rightleftharpoons FeSCN^{2+}(aq) \tag{25-3}$$

and the equilibrium constant expression is:

$$K = \frac{[FeSCN^{2+}]}{[Fe^{3+}][SCN^-]} \tag{25-4}$$

Le Chatelier's principle tells you that increasing the concentration of one of the ions, say SCN^-, will cause the balance of the system to shift in such a way as to restore the ratio in Equation *25-4*. The added thiocyanate will speed up the rate of the forward reaction, reducing the concentration of iron(III) and increasing the concentration of the complex, thus restoring K to its previous value.

Of course, if too much of one of the reactants or products is added, the system can be overpowered and will be unable to restore the equilibrium condition. You will use this to your advantages as part of your investigation. In this experiment, you will prepare five equilibrium mixtures of $Fe^{3+}(aq)$ and $SCN^-(aq)$ ions, plus a standard, for which the concentration of the complex is known. You will then use a colorimeter unit to measure the intensity of the red color of the complex. Here's how it works. The solutions you will prepare have a red color. That means that when ordinary "white" light is passed through the solution, other colors are absorbed but the red is transmitted. In effect, the other colors are filtered out by the solution. The colorimeter sends a beam of monochromatic (one-color) light through a sample of the solution being tested. The particular color chosen is one that the colored species in the solution (the $FeSCN^{2+}$ complex) will absorb; in this case, it will be blue light, with wavelength of 470 nm.[1] The beam is passed through the sample, then the colorimeter measures the intensity of the blue light that is transmitted; the rest is absorbed by the solution. The greater the concentration of the $FeSCN^{2+}$ complex of the solution, the more blue light the solution will absorb. It is these values of the *absorbance* (represented by A) that you will use to determine the relative concentrations of $FeSCN^{2+}$ in each of the equilibrium mixtures you will have prepared.

In all, you will test five solutions, plus one *standard* and a *blank*. The blank contains none of the ion whose concentration you are manipulating; the standard is one in which there is such an excess of Fe^{3+} that all of the SCN^- has been converted to the $FeSCN^{2+}$ complex; in other words, it is not an equilibrium system at all. The ratio of the absorbance, A, of each of the equilibrium samples to the absorbance of the standard, A_{std}, will provide you with the information you need to determine the equilibrium concentrations of each of the three species in Equation 25-4.

Prelaboratory Assignment

1. Read the entire experiment before coming to the laboratory.

2. Prepare a data table in your notebook similar to the one below.

	Equilibrium Mixtures					Standard
	1	2	3	4	5	6
Absorbance						
Composition						
Absorbance						

Temperature of equilibrium systems: _____ °C

Prelaboratory Questions

1. Calculate the mole ratio of iron(III) to thiocyanate before mixing in each of the five standards, beakers 1–5.

2. Calculate the same ratio for beaker 6, the reference solution.

3. Explain why it is reasonable to assume that all of the thiocyanate ion in beaker 6 has been converted to thiocyanatoiron(III) complex.

4. Why is it necessary to know the temperature of the equilibrium systems?

5. Questions 3 and 4 of Analysis and Conclusions each contain a parenthetical (Why?). Answer those three questions (there are two such in #4).

---

[1] nm = nanometer; 1 nm = 10^{-9}m

Safety Precautions

1. Chemical splash-protective eyewear must be worn at all times in the laboratory.

2. **Caution: strong acid.** The iron(III) nitrate solutions were made using 1.0 M nitric acid, HNO_3, as the solvent. Acids are corrosive to skin and clothing. Rinse and wipe up all spills immediately with large quantities of water.

3. **Thiocyanate solutions are moderately toxic** and generate highly-toxic hydrogen cyanide gas if heated strongly. Avoid contact and wash your hands thoroughly with soap and water before leaving the laboratory.

Materials

Apparatus

spectrophotometer/colorimeter,
   interfaced or stand-alone
cuvettes with lid (7, if available)
tissues, lint-free (such as Kim Wipes)
pipets, graduated 5 mL or larger (3)
pipet bulb
beakers (6), 30–50-mL
   (for samples and standard, plus
   three others to hold reagent stock solutions)
beaker, 150-mL or larger, for waste
thermometer

Reagents

potassium thiocyanate, KSCN, 0.0020 *M*
iron(III) nitrate, $Fe(NO_3)_3$, 0.0020 M (in 1.0 *M*
   HNO_3)
iron(III) nitrate, $Fe(NO_3)_3$, 0.200 M (in 1.0 *M*
   HNO_3)
distilled water (wash bottle)
nitric acid, 1.0 *M*, for blank

Procedure

In small, clean separate beakers, obtain samples of 0.0020 *M* KSCN, 0.0020 *M* $Fe(NO_3)_3$, and 0.200 *M* $Fe(NO_3)_3$. Be very careful to distinguish between the 0.0020 *M* and 0.200 *M* $Fe(NO_3)_3$ solutions. You will need about 30–35 mL of the 0.0020 *M* $Fe(NO_3)_3$, and about 20 mL of each of the other two.

Part A: Preparation of Standard and Equilibrium Mixtures

Note: Because the value of *K*, the equilibrium constant, varies with temperature, note and record the temperature of any one of your stock solutions. This will be assumed to be the equilibrium temperature for each of the equilibrium mixtures.

1. Label your six sample beakers, 1–6. Prepare the samples and standard as follows, using pipettes. Once begun, this process should be done in a relatively smooth, efficient manner since the color of the equilibrium mixtures will fade over time.

   Note: Graduated cylinders do not give sufficiently precise volumes, so are not a satisfactory substitute for this experiment.

	$Fe(NO_3)_3$ 0.0020 *M*	KSCN 0.0020 *M*	H_2O (distilled)
Beaker 1:	5.00 mL	1.00 mL	4.00 mL
Beaker 2:	5.00	2.00	3.00
Beaker 3:	5.00	3.00	2.00
Beaker 4:	5.00	4.00	1.00
Beaker 5:	5.00	5.00	0.00

Beaker 6: (Standard) 9.00 mL 0.200 M $Fe(NO_3)_3$ + 1.00 mL 0.0020 *M* KSCN

Part B: Determining the Composition of Equilibrium Mixtures

2. Prepare a blank by filling a clean cuvette with 1.0 M HNO_3 to 3/4 of its capacity. Place the cap on the cuvette, wipe the smooth faces with a tissue, and place the cuvette in the slot. Follow the directions for your spectrophotometer/colorimeter to calibrate the instrument at 470 nm.

3. Follow the following procedure with each of your six samples. If it is necessary to reuse the same cuvette, it should be rinsed several times with distilled or deionized water after each use. If you have enough cuvettes to complete the analyses without reusing them, set each one aside after use until you are ready to follow the Disposal procedure. Do so in such a way that you can clearly identify each sample cuvette, in case you feel it necessary to re-check a result.

   Depending on your particular instrumentation, it may be possible for you to have the data stored for later analysis. (Interfaced units can all do this.) Even so, it is recommended that you record the values directly in your data table as they are collected.

   Rinse a clean cuvette with two 1-mL (approximately) portions of the mixture from beaker 1, discarding the rinsings in your waste beaker.

   Fill the cuvette to the appropriate level, about 3/4 full for plastic cuvettes. Cap the cuvette and wipe the outer surface with a lint-free tissue or cloth. Make sure you touch only the ribbed or opaque sides of the cuvette.

   Insert the cuvette in the sample holder of your spectrophotometer/colorimeter and determine the absorbance (A) given by the instrument. Remove the cuvette from the sample holder of the instrument and set it aside unless it is to be cleaned and reused.

   Follow the same sequence of steps with each of the mixtures, 2–6.

Disposal

1. Pour the contents of your cuvettes and remaining stock reagents into a large (250-mL or larger) beaker. Slowly and with stirring, add baking soda to neutralize the nitric acid in the iron(III) nitrate and complex ion solutions. When no additional foaming occurs upon addition of baking soda, the solution may be rinsed down the drain with large amounts of water or disposed of as your teacher directs.

2. Rinse the cuvettes several times with distilled or deionized water and place them, mouth-down, on paper towels to dry, unless your teacher directs otherwise.

3. Wash remaining glassware and rinse with tap water and/or distilled water and return all items to their proper place. Glass pipets should be allowed to dry in a vertical position, tips up, after rinsing with distilled or deionized water.

4. Wash your hands thoroughly before leaving the laboratory.

Analysis and Conclusions

Prepare a Summary Table in your notebook with the headings shown below. Questions 1–5 will lead you through the necessary calculations to fill in your table. Note that the concentrations will change from sample to sample, except for those of the standard, and because the standard is not an equilibrium system, there will be no value written for K.

Beaker	$[Fe^{3+}]_{eq}$	$[SCN^-]_{eq}$	$[FeSCN^{2+}]_{eq}$	K

1. In beaker 6, the concentration of thiocyanate ion is assumed to be 0: all of the thiocyanate has been converted to $FeSCN^{2+}$. Calculate the concentration of the complex in beaker 6.

2. In each of the five equilibrium mixtures, the absorbance of the solution is in direct proportion to the concentration of $FeSCN^{2+}$ in the mixture. Since the concentration of complex in the standard is known, its concentration in each of the other beakers is given by the relation:

$$[FeSCN^{2+}]_{eq} = \frac{A_{eq}}{A_{std}}[FeSCN^{2+}]_{std} \qquad (25\text{-}5)$$

where the subscripts, *eq* and *std*, represent the absorbance values for the equilibrium mixtures and the standard, respectively. Thus, A_{std} is always the same, while A_{eq} is different for each mixture.

Calculate the equilibrium concentrations of $FeSCN^{2+}$ in each of the five equilibrium mixtures and add that information to the Summary Table. Show the calculation for beaker 1 in your notebook, then simply list the results for each of the other four equilibrium mixtures in your Summary Table.

3. The initial concentration of iron(III) ion is the same in all of the first five beakers. (Why?) Remembering that in each mixture 5.00 mL of 0.0200 M Fe^{3+} ion was diluted to 10.00 mL total volume, calculate the concentration of Fe^{3+} in each beaker.

4. The initial (before reaction) concentration of SCN⁻ in beaker 5 is the same as the value you calculated for $[Fe^{3+}]$ in question 3. (Why?) In beakers 1–4, the values for [SCN⁻] are equal to the *difference between* the initial concentration and the value of $[FeSCN^{2+}]$ for each trial. (Why?)

5. **a.** Write the equilibrium law expression for the reaction.
    b. Calculate the value of the equilibrium constant, *K*, for each of the trials 1–5, using the equilibrium concentrations of each species for each trial.

    Note: The following calculations are readily done with a graphing calculator, but the questions are based on the assumption that you will do them manually. If you use a graphing calculator, replace the average deviation in steps 7 and 8 with the standard deviation function ("stdDev" on Texas Instruments™ calculators, such as the TI-84+) of your calculator.

6. Determine the mean (arithmetic average) value for the equilibrium constant, *K*. If you find that one of your values for *K* is significantly different from the others, it is permissible to omit that value from the determination of the mean. If you do so, you must also omit that value from the next question. One test for deciding whether or not to do this is to average the other four values, then check to see if the fifth value is more than 10% away from the average of the four "good" values. *If you do omit a value, you must say so and justify doing so.* Only one value can be omitted in this way; if you have more than one to omit, your experimental precision was not good (probably due to sample preparation). You might consider repeating the entire experiment.

7. Calculate the absolute value of the difference between the average value for *K* and each of the five individual values, then determine the average of these five values, the average deviation for your value of *K*.

8. One test of the precision of a series of determinations is to calculate the percentage by which the values deviate. Determine the percentage of your mean value of *K* that is represented by the standard deviation. Reasonably enough, this is referred to as your percent deviation.

    While it is normal to want the highest possible level of precision, and therefore the smallest possible percent deviation, equilibrium constant determinations are sufficiently sensitive to even slight variations in conditions that any case in which the percent deviation doesn't exceed 10% is to be deemed quite successful.

9. Suggest an explanation for the fact that you were directed to calculate values of *K* for beakers 1–5, but not for beaker 6.

10. Use your experimental data to determine the value of ΔG° for the reaction system.

11. Suppose you carried out the same experiment using solutions that had been chilled to a temperature significantly lower than room temperature. Explain how you could use the value of K at the lower temperature to determine whether the reaction between iron(III) ion and thiocyanate ion was endothermic or exothermic.

Experiment 26

Determination of a Solubility Product Constant

Introduction

In this experiment the K_{sp} of calcium iodate will be determined using gravimetric titration. The concentration of iodate ion in a saturated solution will be determined by first converting the iodate ion to triiodide ion in acidic solution and then titrating the triiodide ion to a colorless starch end point with sodium thiosulfate. The net-ionic, *unbalanced* equations for the reactions are shown below.

$$IO_3^-(aq) + I^-(aq) \rightarrow I_3^-(aq) \qquad (26\text{-}1)$$

$$S_2O_3^{2-}(aq) + I_3^-(aq) \rightarrow S_4O_6^{2-}(aq) + I^-(aq) \qquad (26\text{-}2)$$

A solution of sodium thiosulfate is prepared; the masses of the solute and of the solution are known, so that the concentration of thiosulfate ion, in mol $S_2O_3^{2-}$(aq)/g of solution, can be determined to three-significant figure precision. This will be the titrant.

Separately, a sample of saturated calcium iodate will be diluted and acidified, then an excess of iodide ion will be added, converting the iodate quantitatively to triiodide ion, I_3^-. This solution will then be titrated with the thiosulfate solution just prepared. To avoid over-shooting the endpoint of this titration, a small sample of the triiodide solution will be reserved. The reserved amount is called a *titration thief*. Once the bulk of the triiodide solution has been titrated, the thief will be returned to the titration vessel and the resulting mixture will be titrated to completion.

You are to carry out three separate trials, perform the calculations for each trial, then calculate the mean value and average deviation. Use the mean value in answering #7 of **Analysis and Conclusions**.

Prelaboratory Assignment

1. Read the entire experiment before you begin.

2. Prepare a Data Table in your notebook in which to record the titration data for each of your three titrations.

Prelaboratory Questions

1. Write the balanced equation for the dissolving of calcium iodate, $Ca(IO_3)_2$, in water. Show this process as an equilibrium.

2. How will the concentrations of calcium ion and iodate ion in solution compare?

3. The titration reactions are carried out in the presence of acid. Write the equation for the reaction you would expect calcium ion to undergo in the presence of excess hydroxide ion. This is one of the reasons for acidifying the titration mixtures (step 2).

4. Balance the two reactions given in the Introduction. You will need these in carrying out your post-lab calculations, in Analysis and Conclusions. The reactions take place in acidic solution.

Safety Precautions

1. Chemical splash-protective eyewear must be worn at all times in the laboratory.

2. All of the solutions in this experiment are eye and skin irritants. Gloves are recommended.

Materials

Apparatus

milligram or centigram balance
50-mL beakers (4)
30-mL dropper bottle
calibrated (or volumetric) pipette, 2.50 mL
thin-stem pipettes, for titration thief (3)

Reagents

sodium thiosulfate pentahydrate crystals
distilled water (wash bottle)
saturated calcium iodate solution
hydrochloric acid, HCl(aq), 2 M
potassium iodide solid, KCl(s)
starch solution in thin-stem pipette

Procedure

1. Weigh out between 0.18 and 0.20 grams ($\pm$ 1 mg) of sodium thiosulfate pentahydrate in a tared 50-mL beaker. Add about 10 mL of distilled water. Record the mass of the solution. Stir until fully dissolved. Add the solution to a 30-mL dropper bottle. (This is called a *weight buret*.) Record the mass of the weight buret and solution.

   Calculate the concentration of the solution in moles of sodium thiosulfate pentahydrate per gram of solution, mol $S_2O_3{}^{2-}$/g solution. Do this calculation as part of your observations, before you proceed.

2. Prepare three calcium iodate samples as follows:

   Add about 20 mL of water to a 50-mL beaker. Pipette 2.50 mL of saturated calcium iodate solution into the beaker. Add 10 drops of 2 M HCl, followed by about 0.2 grams of potassium iodide and swirl until all is dissolved. Carry out steps 3 and 4 with each sample. Use a clean thin-stem pipet for each titration thief, to avoid contamination.

3. Remove about 1 mL of the solution in a thin-stem pipette (the bulb of the pipette holds 3.5 mL). (This is the *titration thief* mentioned in the Introduction.) Set the pipette aside for later use. Your solution should be a somewhat yellow-brown color, due to presence of triiodide ion.

4. Add liquid from your weight buret until a light-yellow color is reached. Add 10 drops of starch solution. Titrate to colorless with thiosulfate from your weight buret. Add the solution from the titration thief and titrate very carefully to colorless. Swirl the titration mixture after each addition from the weight buret to ensure that you don't overshoot the endpoint. Weigh your weight buret again to determine the mass of thiosulfate solution used. Note and record the temperature of your titration mixture; presumably the reaction was carried out isothermally at this temperature.

Analysis and Conclusions

Three analyses were carried out; the directions that follow refer to one of the three. For each of the calculations called for, you are to show how each answer is obtained for the first titration. You may simply report the results of the calculations for the other two trials. Label each value clearly.

1. Calculate the concentration of your sodium thiosulfate solutions in mol $S_2O_3^{2-}$/g solution.

2. Calculate the moles of thiosulfate solution used in each titration.

3. Calculate the moles of iodate ion present in the saturated solution. Be sure to take into account the stoichiometry of the two redox reactions that are involved in the titration.

4. Use the number of moles of iodate present and the volume of saturated solution used to determine the molar concentrations of iodate ion and calcium ion in the saturated calcium iodate solution.

5. Calculate the K_{sp} for calcium iodate for each trial.

6. Determine the mean value for K_{sp} of calcium iodate and the average deviation for your three trials.

   (Note: Do not be alarmed if your average deviation approaches 100%; large variations, up to an order of magnitude, are normal in K_{sp} calculations, even when carried out under the most exacting conditions.)

7. Prepare a summary table showing concentration of thiosulfate solution, concentrations of calcium and iodate ions, and K_{sp}, *for each trial*, as well as the average value for K_{sp}.

8. The *CRC Handbook of Chemistry and Physics* (1992–3) lists the value of K_{sp} of 6.5×10^{-6} for calcium iodate at 20°C; what is your percent error, based on the average of your three trials?

9. Thermodynamics suggests that there are two principle driving forces in nature: the tendency for systems to seek a state of minimum potential energy, and a tendency toward maximum randomness or disorder.

   a. Based on the average value obtained for K_{sp}, does the position of the equilibrium in the equation that you wrote in Prelaboratory Question 1 appear to favor reactants or products? Explain.

   b. Given the two driving forces:

      i. Would you expect the tendency toward maximum randomness to favor reactants or products? Explain.

      ii. Based on your answer to the previous question, would you expect the value of $\Delta H_{solution}$ for calcium iodate to have a positive or negative sign? That is, would you expect the solution process for $Ca(IO_3)_2(s)$ to be endothermic or exothermic? Defend your answer.

   c. Your titrations were probably carried out at a temperature other that 20°C. Would you expect the value of K_{sp} at your experimental temperature(s) to be greater or less that 6.5×10^{-6}? Explain.

Experiment 27

Electrochemical Cells

Objective

To examine properties of galvanic cells

Concepts

Electrochemistry, oxidation-reduction, activity series, reaction quotients

Introduction

Electrochemistry is the study of the energetics of oxidation-reduction reactions. This topic includes such subjects as batteries, corrosion and reactivities of metals, and electroplating. This experiment will briefly examine some of these topics.

Consider the following reaction equation:

$$Zn(s) + Cu^{2+}(aq) \rightarrow Zn^{2+}(aq) + Cu(s) \qquad (27\text{–}1)$$

When elemental zinc metal is added to a solution of dissolved copper(II) ion, reaction occurs. The metallic zinc dissolves, producing a solution of zinc ion, as metallic elemental copper forms from the copper(II) ion that had been present in solution. This single replacement (or single displacement) reaction can be viewed as the result of two *half-reactions*:

$$Zn(s) \rightarrow Zn^{2+}(aq) + 2e^- \qquad \text{\textit{oxidation}} \qquad (27\text{–}2)$$

$$Cu^{2+}(aq) + 2e^- \rightarrow Cu(s) \qquad \text{\textit{reduction}} \qquad (27\text{–}3)$$

$$Zn(s) + Cu^{2+}(aq) \rightarrow Zn^{2+}(aq) + Cu(s) \qquad \text{\textit{overall}} \qquad (27\text{–}4)$$

The zinc half-reaction is an oxidation, while the copper half-reaction is a reduction. Together they make up the overall net ionic equation for the process.

We can view these reactions as a competition between zinc and copper(II) ions for a pair of electrons. In the zinc/copper reaction, copper(II) has a stronger attraction for two electrons than does zinc, so electrons move from zinc atoms to copper(II) ions, resulting in formation of zinc ions and copper atoms. We say that metallic zinc has *replaced* copper(II) ion in solution. Metallic zinc is *more active* (more *reactive*) than metallic copper, so is more likely to be found combined in compounds than as the free elemental metal. When arranged from most active to least active, the metals form an *electromotive series*, also called an *activity series*. Here is a portion of that series, with activity decreasing left to right.

K, Na, Ba, Ca, Mg, Al, Mn, Zn, Cr, Cd, Fe, Co, Ni, Sn, Pb, *H*, Sb, Bi, As, Cu, Hg, Ag, Pt, Au

Notice that even though hydrogen (H) is not a metal, it has been included in the series. From your text or other experiments you may have learned that one characteristic of acids is the ability to dissolve and react with so-called "active metals," producing metal cations and hydrogen gas. All of the metals to the left of hydrogen in the series above will do this, ones to the right of it will not. The first four in the series will even replace hydrogen from cold water, and the fifth, Mg, will react with hot water. Elements such as gold, silver, and platinum are used in jewelry because of their low reactivity and ability to retain their high luster.

One of the goals of chemistry is to find ways to take advantage of these activity differences. When a piece of metallic zinc is placed in direct contact with a solution of copper(II) ion, electrons flow directly from zinc atoms to copper ions at the point of contact. A far more useful version of this same experiment would be to set up the reaction so that the zinc metal and copper(II) ion solution are *physically separate* from one another (in separate beakers, for example) but are connected *electrically* by a conducting wire. (See Figure 27-1.) Now the electron transfer occurs through the wire, thereby producing an electrical current. We could place a motor or light bulb along the wire joining the zinc/copper beakers and make use of the electrical current produced by the reaction. We have constructed a *voltaic cell* (a battery), consisting of a zinc half-cell and a copper half-cell. A second connection will have to be made between the two beakers to complete the electrical circuit, however. This is necessary in order to maintain charge balance, because the concentration of positive ions is increasing in the oxidation half-cell and decreasing in the reduction half-cell.

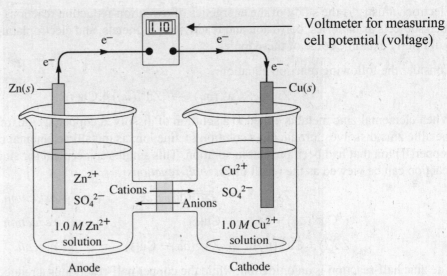

Figure 27-1. Schematic of a zinc/copper voltaic cell. Electrons flow spontaneously through the wire from the zinc half-cell to the copper half-cell when the switch is closed. Ions move to/from the salt bridge to compensate for the change in positive charge in the half cells.

In common practice, a U-shaped glass tube containing a nonreactive salt solution (a *salt bridge*) is used to do this, or, alternatively, a porous porcelain cup is used to contain one half-reaction, and is then placed in a beaker containing the second half-reaction.

In voltaic cells, reactions are always spontaneous and will proceed in the direction that gives a positive cell potential (voltage). They are spontaneous and *exergonic*[1]. They take place with the *release* of energy. This energy can be put to use if the cell is set up correctly.

In order to cause a system to move in the nonspontaneous direction, it is necessary to apply an external voltage that exceeds the voltage that would be produced in the spontaneous direction. These endergonic processes are *electrolysis reactions* and take place in an *electrolytic cell*.

---

[1] *Exergonic* is a more general term for release of energy than exothermic, as it can apply to release of energy in any form, not just as heat. Its opposite is *endergonic*.

A relationship known as the Nernst equation describes the effect of concentration on the electrical potential of a cell. The equation is:

$$E_{cell} = E_{cell}^0 - \frac{RT}{nF} \ln Q \qquad (27\text{--}5)$$

where R is 8.31 J/mol•K, T is the absolute temperature, n is the number of moles of electrons transferred in the reaction, and F is the Faraday constant, 96, 485 Coulombs of charge per mole of electrons. For processes occurring at 1 atm pressure and 298 K ("standard conditions"), and using the conversion between natural and common logarithms, $\ln Q = 2.303 \log Q$, the equation becomes:

$$E_{cell} = E_{cell}^0 - \frac{0.0591}{n} \log Q \qquad (27\text{--}6)$$

where Q is the reaction quotient and has the same form as the equilibrium law expression for the system. (Note: Many sources, including the reference tables that accompany the AP Chemistry test, round this to 0.0592, rather than 0.0591.)

In this experiment, you will examine the relative reactivity of some metals and verify a small portion of the electromotive series. You will also set up several batteries and measure the voltage delivered by the cells. You will finally study the effect of *concentration* on the potential exhibited by a cell.

Prelaboratory Assignment

1. Read the entire experiment before you begin.

2. Prepare separate data tables for Parts A and B of the procedure.

Prelaboratory Questions

1. Using the table of standard reduction potentials in your textbook, calculate the *standard potential* for the three voltaic cells to be used in Part B: copper/zinc, zinc/magnesium, and copper/magnesium.

2. Examine the form of the Nernst equation, given above. For the reaction between copper(II) ions and zinc metal, producing zinc ions and metallic copper:
   a. Write the reaction quotient for the reaction. (Hint: remember that pure solids do not appear in equilibrium law expressions.)
   b. What will happen to the value of the reaction quotient as the reaction between zinc and copper(II) ions continues?
   c. According to the Nernst equation, what should happen to the observed cell potential over time?

3. How do *electrolysis* cells and *voltaic* cells differ? How are they similar?

Safety Precautions

1. Chemical splash-protective eyewear must be worn at all times in the laboratory.

2. Salts of metal ions may be toxic. Wash your hands after using these solutions and dispose of the solutions as directed by your teacher.

3. Sulfuric acid is corrosive. Neutralize spills on the desktop, then clean the area using large amounts of water. For spills on skin and clothing, rinse the affected area with water for several minutes.

Materials

Apparatus

equipment for voltaic cells
    (beakers, porous porcelain cup, voltmeter)
24-well plate

Reagents

1 M sulfuric acid, H_2SO_4(aq)
1 M magnesium sulfate, $MgSO_4$(aq)
1 M copper(II) sulfate, $CuSO_4$(aq)
1 M sodium sulfate, Na_2SO_4(aq)
1 M zinc sulfate, $ZnSO_4$(aq)
0.1 M copper sulfate, $CuSO_4$(aq)
0.1 M zinc sulfate, $ZnSO_4$(aq)
small strips of metallic zinc and copper
magnesium turnings
4-inch strips of magnesium, copper, and zinc

Procedure

Part A: The Electromotive Series

1. In separate wells of the 24-well test plate, add 10 drops of 1 M solutions of each of the following: sulfuric acid, magnesium sulfate, copper(II) sulfate, sodium sulfate, and zinc sulfate. Clean five small strips of metallic zinc with sand paper or steel wool, then place one strip in each well so that the metal is partially covered by the solution in the test plate.

2. Allow the solutions to stand for about 15 minutes. Examine the zinc strips for evidence of reaction, both during the 15-minute waiting period and after, removing them from the test plate wells. Determine which ionic species zinc is capable of *replacing* from solution, and write equations for the reactions that take place.

    Repeat the process using new 10-drop samples of the same solutions, but substituting first copper and then magnesium in place of the zinc metal.

Part B: Voltaic Cells

3. Using strips of copper, zinc, and magnesium metals as electrodes, and solutions of the sulfates of these metals, you will set up three voltaic cells and measure the cell potentials (voltages). The following procedure is described in terms of a copper/zinc voltaic cell. You will also set up copper/magnesium and zinc/magnesium voltaic cells.

4. Obtain a porous porcelain cup from your instructor and place it in a 400-mL beaker of distilled water for 5 minutes to wet the cup. The porcelain cup is very fragile and expensive: be careful with it.

5. Add 15–20 mL of 1 M $CuSO_4$ to a 100-mL beaker. Obtain a 4-inch strip of copper metal and clean it with sandpaper or steel wool, then wipe the surface clean. Place the copper metal strip into the beaker containing the copper sulfate solution to serve as an electrode.

    Remove the porcelain cup from the water bath, and add 10–15 mL of 1 M $ZnSO_4$ to the cup. Obtain a 4-inch strip of zinc metal and clean it with sandpaper. Place the zinc metal strip into the porous cup containing the zinc sulfate solution to serve as an electrode.

    Connect one lead of the voltmeter to the copper strip, and connect the other lead of the voltmeter to the zinc strip.

    Place the porous cup containing the $Zn|Zn^{2+}$ half-cell into the beaker containing the $Cu|Cu^{2+}$ half-cell. If you get a negative potential (voltage), reverse the clips. Note and record which metal is attached to the positive side of the meter. This is the metal that is being oxidized.

Allow the cell to stand until the voltage reading on the voltmeter has stabilized; then record the *highest* voltage obtained. Allow the system to continue for a period of 10 minutes. Note and record any changes in the observed cell potential.

Set the copper strip aside for use in Part C and dispose of the remaining copper(II) sulfate solution as your teacher directs. Rinse the outside of the porcelain cup, but leave the zinc strip and $ZnSO_4$ solution in place. Replace the copper and $CuSO_4$ with a strip of magnesium and 1 M $MgSO_4$, then use the same method as discussed for the copper/zinc cell to construct a cell consisting of magnesium/magnesium sulfate and zinc/zinc sulfate. Note and record the highest voltage obtained. As before, if you get a negative potential (voltage), reverse the clips. Note and record which metal is attached to the positive side of the meter. This is the metal that is being oxidized. You need not let this one run an extra 10 minutes.

Finally, dispose of the remaining zinc sulfate solution as your teacher directs, rinse the porcelain cup thoroughly with distilled water, and fill the cup with 1 M $CuSO_4$. Clean the copper strip and place it in the cup with the $CuSO_4$. Note and record the highest voltage obtained and which metal is being oxidized.

Part C: Effect of Concentration on Cell Potential

6. Prepare a copper/zinc voltaic cell as in Part B, using 1 M $ZnSO_4$ solution as before, but replace the 1 M $CuSO_4$ solution with 0.1 M $CuSO_4$ solution. Measure the voltage of the cell. How does the decrease in concentration of copper ion affect the voltage of the cell?

Prepare a copper/zinc voltaic cell as in Part 2, using 1 M $CuSO_4$ solution as before, but replace the 1 M $ZnSO_4$ solution with 0.1 M $ZnSO_4$ solution. Measure the voltage of the cell. Does the decrease in concentration of Zn^{2+} ion affect the voltage measured? How? Why?

7. Prepare a voltaic cell as in Part 2, only using $Cu|Cu^{2+}$ (1 M) as one half-cell and $Cu|Cu^{2+}$ (0.1 M) as the other half-cell. Measure the voltage of this cell. Why does the cell show a potential difference? What is the "driving force" in this cell? This type of cell is sometimes called a "concentration cell."

Analysis and Conclusions

1. List the metals from Part A in order of increasing activity, citing experimental results to defend the order you assign. Compare your experimental results with the activity series given in the Introduction. Account for any discrepancies.

2. For each of the cells used in Part B:
    a. Report the values obtained for the cell potentials of each of the three cells, then calculate the percentage *difference* between your experimentally determined voltage and the standard voltage. Suggest possible explanations for any major differences.

    b. Identify the metal being oxidized in each cell. The cation of the other metal must have been reduced. Write the net ionic equations for the reactions that occurred in each cell.

3. In Prelaboratory Question 2 you predicted what would happen to the observed cell potential as the cell continued to operate. Was your prediction successful? How dramatic was the effect (if any)?

4. Using the Nernst equation, calculate Q for each of the concentration cells used in Part C. Use your values of Q and the calculated standard cell potentials for each system to calculate the expected voltage in each case. Compare your experimental results with those predicted by your calculations. (Hint: What would be the value of E^0 for the cell in step 7 of Part C? Why?)

Experiment 28

Electrolysis and Electrolytic Cells

Objective

To examine the products of three different electrolytic cell systems

Concepts

Oxidation and reduction, electrolysis, competing reactions

Introduction

Electrolysis involves the use of an electrical current to force a chemical reaction to proceed in a direction in which it would not proceed spontaneously. While Galvanic cells take advantage of spontaneous oxidation-reduction reactions to produce useful work, electrolytic cells must be driven. When an electrical current is passed through a molten or dissolved electrolyte between two physically separated electrodes, two chemical changes take place. At the positive electrode (called the *anode*), an oxidation half-reaction takes place. At the negative electrode (the *cathode*), a reduction half-reaction takes place. Exactly what half-reaction occurs at each electrode is determined by the relative ease of oxidation–reduction of all the species present in the electrolysis cell. In this experiment you will study the electrolysis of three systems: a solution of copper(II) chloride, distilled water, and a solution of potassium iodide.

The apparatus involved is simple and the procedure is very straightforward. Your primary concern is to make careful observations of what transpires at each of the electrodes in each of the cell systems. Color changes, evidence of gas evolution, and detectable odors all will play a role in helping you determine what is taking place in each case. The electrolytic cell consists of a U-shaped glass tube into which you will place the liquid or solution to be electrolyzed. The electrodes may be ordinary pencil leads or pieces of wire. The source of the electric current used to drive the reactions is a 9-volt dry cell battery.

In Part A, you will carry out the electrolysis of a solution of copper(II) chloride. You will be looking for evidence to show that the current separated the copper(II) chloride into its constituent elements.

The second system to be investigated is what happens when pure water is decomposed. Because water is a very weak electrolyte, it will be necessary to add a strong electrolyte to the water. Sodium sulfate is chosen to serve this purpose because the ions that make it up are harder to oxidize and reduce than the water. The only function of the sodium sulfate is to improve current flow.

The final system, a solution of potassium iodide, will illustrate the fact that when more than one possible oxidation or reduction can occur, it will always be the one that requires the least input of electrical energy that will take place.

Prelaboratory Assignment

1. Read the entire experiment before coming to the laboratory.

2. Set up a two-column section for each part of the experiment in which to list your observations of changes occurring at the cathode and anode in each system. Recall that you're looking for evidence of reaction that might include color change, evolution of gas, and formation of deposits on the electrode tip(s).

Prelaboratory Questions

1. Consult the table of standard reduction potentials in your text to complete this table, showing the half-reactions and corresponding half-cell potentials for the possible cathode and anode reactions that can occur in the three parts of this experiment. Note that water is always available to be oxidized or reduced, and remember that you will need to reverse equations from the table to get your oxidation half-reactions. One line has been filled in for you because the half-reaction in question does not appear in your text.

Part A	Reduction Half-Reactions		E^o
H_2O			
Cu^{2+}			
Part A	Oxidation Half-Reactions		E^o
H_2O			
Cl^-			
Part B	Reduction Half-Reactions		E^o
H_2O			
Na^+			
Part B	Oxidation Half-Reactions		E^o
H_2O			
SO_4^{2-}	$2SO_4^{2-} \rightarrow S_2O_8^{2-} + 2e^-$		-2.01 V
Part C	Reduction Half-Reactions		E^o
H_2O			
K^+			
Part C	Oxidation Half-Reactions		E^o
H_2O			
I^-			

Safety Precautions

1. Chemical splash-protective eyewear must be worn at all times in the laboratory.

2. A 9-volt transistor battery will be used as the source of electrical current for the electrolysis. Be aware that even a small battery can cause an electrical shock if care is not exercised.

3. Potassium iodide may be irritating to the skin. Avoid contact.

4. Elemental iodine will stain the skin and clothing.

Materials

Apparatus

U-tube or 16-cm piece of glass tubing
Bunsen burner with flame spreader
9-volt battery
carbon electrodes or pencil leads
wire connector cords with alligator clips
   or a special battery clip with alligator leads
pipets for adding reagent solutions to U-tube
beaker or other container for waste
wash bottle with distilled water for cleaning tube

Reagents

copper(II) chloride, $CuCl_2$(aq), 1 M
distilled water with Na_2SO_4(aq), 0.5 M
potassium iodide, KI(aq), 0.5 M
bromothymol blue indicator
starch solution
phenolphthalein indicator

Procedure

Part A: Electrolysis of Copper(II) Chloride

1. Use a pipet to fill your U-tube to within about 0.5 cm of the top. To avoid air bubbles, insert the stem of the filled pipet as far as you can, then slowly expel liquid into the glass tube as you withdraw the pipet.

2. Attach the connector cords to the electrodes and insert one electrode into each side of the U-tube. Connect the other ends of the cords to the positive and negative terminals of the battery. See Figure 28-2.

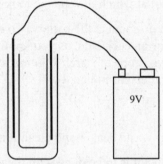

Figure 28-2. Electrolysis Apparatus

As the reaction in the tube proceeds, look for changes in the color of the solution—appearance of copper metal (seen as an orange-brown coloration) on one of the electrode tips—and see if you can detect the odor of gaseous chlorine on one side or the other. Be sure to connect each observation you record with either the cathode (negative) or anode (positive) of the system. You will find a $\oplus$ symbol identifying the positive post of the battery.

3. When you have decided that no further changes are taking place, disconnect the battery. Remove the electrodes and examine each for any further evidence of change, then discard them unless your teacher directs you to do otherwise.

   Note: If you are using wire electrodes, they are to be cleaned between uses and reused for each part of the procedure. Do not discard them unless and until your teacher directs you to do so.

   Empty the contents of the U-tube into your waste beaker then rinse the tube several times with distilled water from your wash bottle. Proceed to Part B.

Part B: Electrolysis of Distilled Water

4. In a small beaker, mix a few milliliters of the distilled water-Na_2SO_4 mixture with a few drops of bromothymol blue indicator, just enough to give a distinct color. Bromothymol blue is yellow at pH values below 6, and turns blue at pH 8 and above. Because the solution in your beaker is neither acidic nor basic, the color should be green. Use a clean pipet to fill the U-tube with the green solution, as you did with the copper(II) chloride in step 2.

5. Using fresh electrodes, attach the wire connectors to the electrodes, insert the electrodes into the tube, and connect the battery. As you observe changes that occur, look for differences in the size of bubbles generated at the two electrodes and look for changes in the color of the indicator. Does there appear to be any material collecting on either of the electrode tips this time?

    When you have seen all the changes, which shouldn't take more than a couple of minutes, try reversing the polarity by switching the sides for the electrodes. Do the changes reverse? Should they? Does the reversal happen right away?

    Empty the tube into your waste beaker and clean it as before (step 4), to get it ready for Part C.

Part C: Electrolysis of Potassium Iodide

6. Fill the U-tube with 0.5 M KI(aq), to within about 0.5 cm of the top. As you did in the previous parts of the procedure, attach the wire connectors to fresh electrodes, insert the electrodes into each side of the tube, and connect to the battery. Allow the current to flow for about 5–8 minutes, noting any changes that occur. As before, be sure to associate each observed change with the electrode (cathode or anode) at which the change took place.

7. Remove the electrodes and disconnect the battery. To each side of the tube, add one or two drops of phenolphthalein indicator on each side; as you know, this is a test for the presence of excess hydroxide ion. Now add two drops of starch solution to each side of the tube. A blue-black color indicates the presence of molecular iodine, I_2.

Disposal

1. Empty the U-tube into your waste beaker and clean it as described for Parts A and B.

2. Consult your teacher as to what is to be done with the contents of the waste beaker.

3. Your teacher will direct you as to what to do with your glass U-tube, the wire connectors, and the battery. The electrodes may be discarded unless you were using pieces of wire, in which case your teacher will tell you what to do with them.

Analysis and Conclusions

Part A

1. Cite specific evidence from Part A that clearly identifies the products of the reaction as being metallic copper and gaseous, elemental chlorine.

2. Consult your table from the Prelaboratory Question to write: (a) the oxidation half-reaction that occurred; (b) the reduction half-reaction that occurred; and (c) the overall, complete ionic equation for the reaction in Part A.

3. What is the minimum voltage that the battery had to supply to cause this reaction to occur? Show calculations to defend your answer.

Part B

4. At the conclusion of the electrolysis, the liquid in the tube is blue on one side and yellow on the other.
    a. What ion must be present to cause the blue color to appear?
    b. What ion must be present to cause the yellow color to appear?

5. Look at your answers to **4a** and **4b**. Based on the rate at which they formed, what gas was produced at the same electrode as hydrogen ions? What gas was produced where hydroxide ions appeared?

    Complete the following half-reactions. Indicate which occurs at the anode and which occurs at the cathode.

    $4\,e^- + 4\,H_2O(l) \rightarrow$ _____ $+\ 4\,OH^-(aq)$ (anode/cathode)

    $2\,H_2O(l) \rightarrow$ _____ $+\ 4\,H^+(aq) + 4\,e^-$ (anode/cathode)

6. You are familiar with the terms "exothermic" and endothermic.
    a. Is the electrolysis of water an endothermic or exothermic process? Explain.
    b. How would you expect the amount of energy needed to decompose water to compare with the amount of energy released when hydrogen and oxygen gases react to produce water? Assume the same number of moles of water is involved in each case. Explain the logic used to formulate your answer to this question.

Part C

7. Based on your tests with phenolphthalein and starch, what were the products of the oxidation half-reaction? The reduction half-reaction?

8. Select from your list in the Prelaboratory Question the equations for the two half-reactions. Write them, along with their respective E° values, then combine them to get the overall reaction equation for the electrolysis of aqueous potassium iodide. What is the minimum voltage required to cause this reaction to take place? Show calculations to support your answer.

9. Explain why copper(II) ion was reduced to copper metal in Part A, but potassium ion was not reduced to potassium metal in Part C.

10. What would have been the minimum voltage required in order for the products to be:
    a. Metallic potassium and molecular iodine?
    b. Metallic potassium and oxygen gas?
    c. Hydrogen gas and molecular iodine?

Experiment 29

Synthesis and Analysis of an Iron Compound

Objective

To carry out the synthesis of a compound, then analyze it to determine its composition

Concepts

Synthesis, hydrates, oxidation-reduction titrations, spectrophotometry

Introduction

In this experiment you will synthesize an unknown compound of iron, then use a series of analytical techniques to determine the formula of the compound that you have synthesized. The quantities you will use are extremely small, so great care must be taken throughout the procedure. This is your final laboratory examination, incorporating many of the techniques you have learned this year. You may also be asked to do some extra work with the reaction system(s); that will be the in-class portion of the exam, during the assigned examination time.

- All glassware used should be heat tolerant.
- Water always means distilled or deionized water.
- When masses are given, try to get as close to the specified amount as you can but if the directions say "about," then an estimate will do; less is better in such cases.

Prelaboratory Assignment

1. Read the entire experiment before you begin. Review the various techniques and procedures in other experiments.

2. Prepare a suitable table for recording the data for Part A.

Safety Precautions

1. Safety goggles that give chemical-splash protection must be worn at all times in the laboratory.

2. Observe the usual precautions when using heating devices.

3. Sulfuric acid solutions are corrosive to skin and clothing. Wipe up all spills with large amounts of water. Use baking soda to neutralize spills on the bench-top, but not on your skin.

Materials

Part A: Synthesis of Unknown Compound

Apparatus
balance, milligram or analytical
10 x 100 mm test tube (2)
cork or stopper for one of the tubes
hot plate or similar heating device
wooden applicator stick or plastic stir-straw
pipet, microtip plastic or glass Pasteur, with bulb

Reagents
distilled water (wash bottle)
iron(III) chloride hexahydrate, $FeCl_3 \cdot 6H_2O$
potassium oxalate monohydrate, $K_2C_2O_4 \cdot H_2O$
ethyl alcohol, 95%, ice-cold (wash bottle)
acetone, ice-cold (wash bottle)

Part B: Analysis of Product

Apparatus

drying oven
desiccator
volumetric flask, 25-mL or similar (2)
microtip plastic pipets (3)
small beakers or flasks (10-25 mL)
    as titration vessels
volumetric pipets

Reagents

sulfuric acid, H_2SO_4, 0.20 M
sulfuric acid, H_2SO_4, 6 M
potassium permanganate, $KMnO_4$(aq),
    ($\sim$ 2 x 10^{-5} mol $KMnO_4$/gram of solution)
standard iron(II) solution, 0.025 mg Fe^{2+}/mL
ammonium acetate, 1 M
hydroxylammonium chloride, 1 M
1,10-phenanthroline (o-phenanthroline)

Procedure

Part A: Synthesis of the Unknown Compound

1. Dissolve 0.250 g of solid iron(III) chloride hexahydrate, $FeCl_3 \cdot 6H_2O$, in a previously-weighed 10 x 100 mm tube with about half a milliliter of water. Gentle warming may be necessary to get all of the solid to dissolve. Add more water only as a last resort.

2. Into a separate test tube, place 0.600 g of potassium oxalate monohydrate, $K_2C_2O_4 \cdot H_2O$. Add about 2 mL of water, then use a wood or plastic stick to control the heating as you bring the mixture to near-boiling to dissolve the solid. Try to maintain the temperature just below the boiling point; if boiling begins, remove the tube and contents from the heat.

3. When all of the oxalate has dissolved, pour the solution quickly and quantitatively into the tube containing the ferric chloride solution. Maintain the combined solutions at nearly boiling for a minute or so, noting any changes in appearance of the mixture. Allow the solution to cool; crystals should begin to form. If there is no crystallization, try cooling the tube in ice water. If crystals still do not appear, try scratching the walls of the tube with a glass stirring rod.

4. Remove any remaining supernatant liquid by pulling it up into a clean microtip pipet. As you insert the pipet into the tube, expel most of the air, then gently press the tip against the bottom of the tube and allow the liquid to be pulled up into the pipet. Dispose of the liquid as directed by your teacher.

5. Recrystallize your product by adding about 1 mL of distilled water to the crystals in the tube. Heat to dissolve the crystals, and allow the crystals to form as before, inducing crystallization by cooling or scratching the tube, as necessary. Once again, remove the liquid from the crystals with the same pipet, disposing of the liquid in the same manner as before.

    Add a few drops of ice-cold 95% ethanol to your crystals, agitate the tube briefly, then draw off the ethanol with the pipet.

    Finally, add 5–8 drops of ice-cold acetone to the crystals; this will absorb the last of the water. Acetone may be removed either by pipet or by blowing a stream of dry air into the tube (if air is to be used, the instructor will show you how it is done). Allow the product to air dry overnight (or longer), then weigh the tube and contents to determine the mass of your crystalline product.

Part B: Analysis of the Product

The purpose of this part is to conduct a series of analyses on the product you synthesized in order to determine the relative percentages of the constituent parts, iron(III) ion, oxalate ion, and waters of hydration. From this you will determine the empirical formula of the compound you have prepared. Iron(III) content will be determined spectrophotometrically, oxalate will be determined by redox titration, and the mass of water of hydration present in the crystalline product may be determined directly or by difference.

If you have sufficient product, the number of waters of hydration may be directly determined by heating the product for a minimum of two hours in a $120°C$ oven to drive off the water, followed by cooling in a desiccator.

- The titration and spectrophotometric determination both require a solution of your product.

- The same solution may be used for both parts, and is prepared as follows.

Preparation of the Unknown for Analysis

Dissolve 25–30 mg ($\pm$ 0.1 mg, if possible) of your solid hydrated product, or about 20 mg of anhydrous solid, in a small amount of 0.2 M sulfuric acid in a 25-mL volumetric flask. Once the product is completely dissolved, fill the flask to the mark with 0.2 M sulfuric acid.

6. Determination of Oxalate Ion Content of Product

To determine the mass percentage of oxalate ion in your product, a minimum of three samples are to be titrated with a permanganate solution whose concentration is accurately known, in mol MnO_4^-/g of solution. Your teacher will tell you whether the permanganate solution needs standardization before use.

Label three pipettes: PERM (for permanganate), ACID (for 6 M sulfuric acid), and PROD (for your product). Determine the individual masses of the filled PERM and PROD pipettes to the nearest 0.001 g; the mass of the sulfuric acid pipet is not needed. Place between 1.0 and 1.5 grams of PROD (about $^1/_3$ of the capacity of the pipet) in a clean, dry 10-mL flask and add about 0.5 mL of 6 M sulfuric acid from your ACID pipet. Warm the mixture for 2–3 minutes on a hot plate to between 70° and 80°C, at which point the solution will have started to steam.

While the solution is still hot, begin to add potassium permanganate solution from your PERM pipet, swirling the titration vessel constantly until you have a pink color that persists for at least 30 seconds. It is important that you keep the contents mixed throughout the titration. If drops of permanganate should collect on the sides of the vessel, use a drop or two of H_2SO_4 from your ACID pipette to rinse them down. Record the final masses of the PERM and PROD pipettes.

Repeat the titration twice more, for a total of three trials. You should use a fresh beaker or flask for each trial, but you will want to thoroughly rinse each vessel immediately after use to prevent formation of permanent stains in the glass.

7. Determination of Iron Content of Product

Iron(III) will form a complex ion with 1,10–phenanthroline. This complex absorbs strongly at about 510 nm in the visible range of the spectrum. In this part of the analysis you will form the complex with your product solution, then determine the absorbance of your mixture at 510 nm. By comparing it with a plot of the absorbance of a series of standards, you will determine the relative concentration of iron(II) in your solution.

The analysis will be carried out with a spectrophotometer or colorimeter. See Experiment 11: *Energy Levels and Electron Transitions*, for directions in using the instrument.

You will need the following solutions, which have been prepared for you.
Standard iron(II) solution, 0.025 mg Fe^{2+}/mL
Ammonium acetate, 1 M
Hydroxylammonium chloride, 1 M
1,10-phenanthroline (o-phenanthroline)

8. Preparation of Reference Standards and Unknown

As mentioned above, the determination of iron content is based on formation of a complex ion of iron(II), yet your compound was the result of a precipitation between iron(III) chloride and potassium oxalate. Hydroxylammonium chloride is added to reduce any iron(III) to iron(II), since the 1,10-phenanthroline complex only forms with the 2+ oxidation state of iron; the ammonium acetate is a buffer, which will partially neutralize the acid present in the solution of your product. The complex absorbs strongly at a wavelength of 510 nm.

A set of five reference standards will be used to determine the relationship between iron(II) ion concentration and the amount of light absorbed by the solution at 510 nm. The references will be prepared in 25-mL volumetric flasks; a sixth flask will be used for your unknown. Directions for preparing the five reference solutions follow; the references may be shared with other students, but each will need her or his own product sample.

One milliliter *each* of the ammonium acetate and hydroxylammonium chloride solutions, plus five milliliters of the phenanthroline solution, is placed in each flask. To one of the flasks add (by volumetric pipet) 1.00 mL of the standard iron solution; to another add 2.00 mL; to a third add 3.00 mL; and so on until you have five reference solutions containing from one to five milliliters of the iron standard.

To a sixth flask, add 1.00 mL of your unknown solution remaining from Part A. Fill all six flasks nearly to the mark with water, then allow them to stand for a few minutes while you calibrate the colorimeter and set it for zero absorbance (100% transmission) at 510 nm. Fill the reference solutions (but not the unknown) to the mark, stopper each flask, and invert them several times to ensure mixing. Rinse a cuvette with two 1-mL portions of the first reference solution, then measure its absorbance.

Measure the absorbance of each of the other reference solutions in like fashion, then make a plot of absorbance versus concentration; the plot should be linear. Now fill the flask containing your unknown to the mark and invert to mix, then determine the absorbance of your unknown. By reference to your plot of A versus C, you should be able to arrive at the concentration of iron in your unknown.

Analysis and Conclusions

Oxalate Analysis

1. Before you can determine the concentration of the oxalate, you first need to balance the equation for the reaction, shown below.

$$MnO_4^-(aq) + C_2O_4^{2-}(aq) \rightarrow Mn^{2+}(aq) + CO_2(g)$$

2. For each titration, use your data and the balanced equation to calculate all of the following:
    (i)   The moles of permanganate ion used
    (ii)   The moles of oxalate in each sample
    (iii)   The concentration of oxalate, in mol $C_2O_4^{2-}$/g for your solution

    Do this for each of your samples, then report the average value, as well. If one of your trials differs from the mean of the other two by more than 2%, you may report your average based only on the two "best" trials, but those two must be within 0.5% of each other.

3. Use your average value from question 2 to calculate the moles and mass of oxalate ion that were in the product sample that you used to make your 25.00 mL solution. From this you can calculate the mass percent of oxalate in your product. (Assume the solution has the same density as water.)

4. Calculate the theoretical percentage of oxalate (by mass) in potassium iron(III) oxalate trihydrate $[K_3Fe(C_2O_4)_3 \cdot 3H_2O]$, then calculate the **difference** between this theoretical value and the value you got in question 3. Now calculate the percentage difference between the theoretical value and your experimental percentage of oxalate.

5. Oxalate ion is known to act as a reducing agent; it is possible that the initial reaction that formed your bright-green product was an oxidation-reduction process in which oxalate reduced iron(III) to iron(II), while oxalate was being oxidized to carbon dioxide. Write a balanced equation for the reduction of iron(III) to iron(II) by oxalate ion in acidic solution. Consult a table of standard half-cell potentials to determine whether this reaction is likely to be spontaneous. Could this reaction have taken place?

6. a. Determine the molar excess of oxalate over iron(III) in your synthetic mixture (Part I). [mol oxalate/mol iron(III)]
    b. Is this excess sufficient to account for reduction of iron and for formation of a crystalline iron(II) oxalate monohydrate? Discuss.

Iron Analysis

7. Make a Beer's law plot to determine the concentration of iron in ppm (parts per million), then use that value to calculate the mass percent of iron that was in your unknown, assuming the solution that you used has the same density as water. Remember that the mass of the product that you used was originally dissolved in 25 mL of water, and that one milliliter of that solution was used to make 25 mL of the solution that you analyzed.

8. Calculate the theoretical percentage of iron in $K_3Fe(C_2O_4)_3 \cdot 3H_2O$, then calculate the difference between your experimental result from question 1 and the theoretical percentage for potassium iron(III) oxalate.

AP Experimental Chemistry

Appendix A

Plotting Graphs of Scientific Data

Very often the data collected during experiments are best presented pictorially, by means of a **graph**. This section reviews how graphs are most commonly constructed, but you should consult with your instructor about any special considerations he or she may wish you to include in the graphs you will be plotting in the laboratory.

The use of a graphical presentation allows you to display clearly both experimental data and any relationships that may exist among the data. Graphs also permit interpolation and extrapolation of data, to cover those situations that were not directly investigated in an experiment and to allow predictions to be made for such situations. In order to be meaningful, your *graphs must be well planned*. Study the data before attempting to plot them. By recording all data in tabular form in your notebook, you will be giving yourself organized data from which to prepare your graph.

If you are using a laboratory notebook that has quadrille pages, the notebook itself may be a place to draw your graphs; but for graphs that require interpretation, calculation of slopes, and so on, you need more precise graph paper. You will find several such sheets at the end of this manual. Suggestion: Make a sample graph, either in your notebook or on separate paper, before you transfer it to one of the sheets that have been provided here.

- **Scale Your Data:** A major problem in plotting graphs is deciding what each scale division on the axes of the graph should represent. You must learn to scale your data, so that the graphs you construct will fill virtually the entire graph paper page.

- **Use a Uniform Scale:** Scale divisions on graphs should always be spaced at very regular intervals, usually in units of 10, 100, or some other appropriate power of 10. (Note: the spacing on the vertical axis does not have to be the same as that on the horizontal axis.)

- **Make Scales Clear and Easy to Read:** Each grid line on the graph paper should represent some readily evident number (for example, not 1/3 or 1/4 unit). That's why the graph paper provided is in blocks of 5 x 5 lines.

- **Axes Do Not Have to Start at Zero:** It is not necessary or desirable to have the intersection of the horizontal and vertical axes on your graph always represent the origin (0, 0). For example, if you were plotting temperatures from 100°C to 200°C, it would be silly to start the graph at zero degrees.

- **Label the Axes:** The axes should be labeled in ink as to what they indicate, and the scale divisions should be clearly marked. By studying your data, you should be able to come up with realistic minimum and maximum limits for the scale of the graph and for what each grid line on the graph paper will represent. Consult the many graphs in your textbook for examples of properly constructed graphs.

- **Plot Points Properly and Clearly:** When plotting the actual data points on your graph, use a sharp, hard pencil. Place a single, small round dot to represent each datum. If more than one set of data is being plotted on the same graph, surround each set of points with small circles, squares, or triangles. If an estimate can be made of the probable magnitude of error in the experimental measurements, this can be indicated by **error bars** above and below each data point (the size of the error bars on the vertical scale of the graph should indicate the magnitude of the error on the scale) or by the size of the circles, squares, or triangles.

By convention, the **horizontal** (x) **axis** of a graph is used for plotting the quantity that the experimenter has varied during an experiment (independent variable). The **vertical** (y) **axis** is used for plotting the quantity that is being measured in the experiment (as a function of the other variable). For example, if you were to perform an experiment in which you measured the pressure of a gas sample as its temperature was varied, you would plot temperature on the horizontal axis, since this is the variable that is being controlled by the experimenter. The pressure, which is measured and which results from the various temperatures used, would be plotted on the vertical axis.

To show the relationship between the data points, draw the best possible straight line or smooth curve through the data points. Straight lines should obviously be inked in with a ruler, whereas curves should be sketched using a drafter's French curve.

If the data plot for an experiment is a straight line, you may be asked to calculate the **slope,** and perhaps the **intercept** of the line. Although the best way to determine the slope of a straight line is by the techniques of numerical regression (a graphing calculator will be useful here), if the data seem reasonably linear, the slope may be approximated by:

$$\text{slope} = (y_2 - y_1)/(x_2 - x_1)$$

where (x_1, y_1) and (x_2, y_2) are two points on the line. Once the slope has been determined, either intercept of the line may be determined graphically by extending the line until it intersects the appropriate axis, or by setting y_1 or x_1 equal to zero (as appropriate) in the equation of a straight line:

$$(y_2 - y_1) = (\text{slope})(x_2 - x_1)$$

If your school has computers available for your use, simple computer programs for determining the slope and intercept of linear data are commonly available. In addition, most spreadsheet programs (such as Excel™) also have the ability to plot simple graphs. In fact, the computer may even be set up to plot your data for you on a high-speed printer. Use of computer plots, though, may *not* be permitted by your instructor. The idea is for *you* to learn how to plot data.

Remember *the reason why* graphs are plotted. Although it may seem tedious when you are first learning how to construct them, graphs are intended to *clarify* your understanding of what you have determined in an experiment and to thereby *simplify* interpretation of your results. Rather than just a list of numbers that may seem meaningless, a well-constructed graph can show you instantaneously whether your experimental data exhibit consistency and whether a relationship exists among the variables involved.

Solubility Information

Simple Rules for Solubility of Ionic Compounds in Water

1) Nearly all compounds containing Na^+, K^+, and NH_4^+ are readily soluble in water. (The same generally applies to compounds of Rb; compounds of Li show less-regular behavior.)

2) Nearly all compounds containing NO_3^- are readily soluble in water.

3) Most compounds containing Cl^- are soluble in water, with the common exceptions of $AgCl$, $PbCl_2$, $CuCl$, and Hg_2Cl_2.

4) Most compounds containing SO_4^{2-} are soluble in water, with the common exceptions of $BaSO_4$, $PbSO_4$, and $CaSO_4$.

5) Most compounds containing OH^- ion are *not* readily soluble in water, with the common exceptions of the hydroxides of the alkali metals (Group 1) and $Ba(OH)_2$.

6) Compounds containing CO_3^{2-}, PO_4^{3-}, SO_3^{2-}, and S^{2-} are generally not soluble in water, but Rule 1, above, takes precedence. (**Note:** In the presence of excess acid, these ions are converted to more soluble species, including HCO_3^-, HPO_4^{2-}, $H_2PO_4^-$, HSO_3^-, and HS^-).

7) Most compounds containing other anions not mentioned above either are *not* appreciably soluble in water or do not show discernable patterns.

Appendix C

Vapor Pressure of Water at Various Temperatures

Temperature, °C	Pressure, mm Hg	Temperature, °C	Pressure, mm Hg
0	4.580	31	33.696
5	6.543	32	35.663
10	9.209	34	39.899
15	12.788	36	44.563
16	13.634	38	49.692
17	14.530	40	55.324
18	15.477	45	71.882
19	16.478	50	92.511
20	17.535	55	118.03
21	18.650	60	149.37
22	19.827	65	187.55
23	21.068	70	233.71
24	22.377	75	289.10
25	23.756	80	355.11
26	25.209	85	433.62
27	26.739	90	525.77
28	28.349	95	633.91
29	30.044	100	760.00
30	31.823		

Appendix D

Concentrated Acid–Base Reagent Data

Acids

Reagent	HCl	HNO₃	H₂SO₄	CH₃COOH
Formula weight of solute	36.46	63.01	98.08	60.05
Specific gravity of concentrated reagent	1.19	1.42	1.84	1.05
% concentration	37.2	70.4	96.0	99.8
Molarity	12.1	15.8	18.0	17.4
mL needed for 1 L of 1 M solution	82.5	63.0	55.5	57.5

Bases

Reagent	NaOH	NH₃
Formula weight of solute	40.0	35.06
Specific gravity of concentrated reagent	1.54	0.90
% concentration	50.5	56.6
Molarity	19.4	14.5
mL needed for 1 L of 1 M solution	51.5	69.0

Notes:

- Solutions of sodium hydroxide, NaOH, are normally prepared from solid reagent. The solution data that appear above are primarily for illustrative information

- Data on concentration, density, and amount required to prepare solution will differ slightly from batch to batch of concentrated reagent. Values given here are typical.